SHOOT FOR HEALTHY

"A healthy kitchen provides the foundation for a healthy you."

--Mark Hyman, MD

SHOOT FOR HEALTHY

Chef Patricia Cashion &
Heather Taylor, RDN, LDN

AGOGE FUEL

Chef Patricia Cashion & Heather Taylor

COPYRIGHT

Book Publishing Information
Shoot for Healthy by AGOGE FUEL
ISBN 978-0-692-53755-8

Published by AGOGE FUEL agogefuel.com
To contact the Publisher: agogefuel@gmail.com

DEDICATION PAGE

None of this would be possible without the trust and support of my family, Eric Cashion, my stronghold and best friend; my son, Padraig for putting up with my long hours and always providing me endless love; my bonus children, Cade and Camdin Cashion for welcoming me into their lives with open arms; my parents for their never ending love and support; and of course, to all of my friends and colleagues who have supported my passion to educate in nutrition, using food.

–Chef Patricia Cashion

I dedicate this cook book to all the people who are in search of healing and optimizing their health. I especially dedicate this book to all those who have struggled with health issues and took the challenge to overcome illness with nutrition and lifestyle changes. Your victories are a testament to all those who were told diet and lifestyle don't matter. Your stories are an inspiration to all those who have felt helpless, suffered from drug interactions, and poor medical outcomes. Please continue supporting the fundamental truth that good nutrition is critical for healing, recovery, and longevity. I hope this book continues to support those with the vision and journey toward optimal health.

—Heather Taylor, RDN, LDN

AFFIRMATIONS

*I had the privilege of meeting Patricia through my husband. She has supported and encouraged me throughout my journey to become a healthier me. I was diagnosed with PCOS (polycystic ovarian syndrome) at the age of seventeen. I was informed that my weight would not come off without conventional medicine and that I would never have children. My journey began in November of 2014 when **I contacted Patricia desperately wanting to follow a cleaner eating habit.** I had to know if this would be my way of making my body do what I wanted it to do instead of being a prisoner to my obesity, my disease, my infertility. **She immediately and willingly shared information with me on how to begin the process. I jumped in with both feet and underwent the most drastic change in my life. The recipes were easy to follow and the bonus is they tasted amazing!!! The food did not even make me feel like I was on a specific diet! The past seven months have completely changed my life for the better. I have lost weight, 68 lbs to be exact, without the use of medicine! Then the biggest shock arrived, I finally got my miracle. I am currently four months pregnant and going strong because I was not given up on. Patricia and my husband's support has been a life saving experience for me.** I was on the verge of type 2 diabetes, I could not breathe easily anymore, I had no energy, and my mind was not helping the process. She literally saved my life. The road I was on would have led me to death. Thank you so much Patricia for your love and support. You are my guardian angel.*

--Jenn, Glenville, Georgia

*I have known Patricia for about fifteen years. I always admire her enthusiasm and zest for life. One day she forwarded an article to me from www.marksdailyapple.com. I don't recall the article but it got me thinking and as I poked around further on Mark's site the proverbial "light bulb" went on in my mind. This "Paleo" and "clean eating" stuff makes so much sense. We have shared articles, books and recipes back and forth since that time and I am so proud of her for putting out this cookbook (the first of many, I hope!) **Her passions for healthy food and her family are truly inspiring. I find the recipes included here are easy enough for new cooks to master and tasty enough for seasoned cooks to be proud to serve.** I have several that here that I "go to" often and hope you will find yours as well. Enjoy!*

--Wendy, Cedar Creek, Texas

*For years I suffered with insomnia and other health issues. After following Patricia's clean eating regime and becoming educted on the benefits of a strict, clean diet I can **say that after nearly 20 years I no longer have to use sleeping pills. My skin is better, my digestion is normal, even my mental state is much clearer.***

*Patrcia s a miracle worker. Her food is amazing. **I'm always so shocked at how delicious meals can be with such restrictions, but she does it with ease.** We've been programmed to only consume processed food. I never thought clean eating tasted so incredible. Thank you Patricia.*

--Karith Whirty, Austin, Texas

AFFIRMATIONS

Just imagine thumbing through yet another newly arrived book: they arrive in numbers weekly. Many find their way onto piles for future reading — if and when that should happen. There's a tsunami of information being produced. Not much of it ever grabs imagination.

Just one quick look inside Shoot for Healthy cookbook perked immediate interest. Enough that I couldn't put it down. This book demands attention it's got a lot to say. *And by 'a lot' I mean just that. In truth it takes the place of several books all at the same time. How so?*

My journey into books for learning diet, nutrition and cooking began more than 55 years ago. That's a lot of books over a lot of time. **The delightful frustration is that before Shoot for Healthy cookbook I've never had the joy of everything being under one cover all in one integrated package.** *Before now you'd get nutritional ingredient facts one place, recipes somewhere else, then have to sort through tables of ingredients tracking down nutrient values, combining and calculating them.* **Cashion and Taylor have started a revolution by making life far easier, meal planning far less challenging.**

Pick any page. The dish is named, its ingredient list laid out, preparation instructions given. So far like any other recipe source. Not so fast: note the list of health benefits proudly displayed. To my enchanted liking there's Nutrition Facts looking just like one printed on a package of food: breaking down nutrient ingredients, calories per serving, and grams of carbs, protein and fat.

There comes a time when meal planning is done in relation a diet. Then you want calories and nutrients per serving, total for a meal, daily accumulated totals. Shoot for Healthy cookbook has all that right in its sight: on target.

After 55 years there's now a book I can't say enough about by way of endorsement and recommendation. At last, at long last…

--Ken, Wimberley, Texas
TransEvolutionary Fitness

Chef Patricia has an amzing understanding of the human body and how food can nourish or destroy it. her creaive ideas and expert knowledge on how to use fresh foods in her recipes is exciting. I enjoy everythng that comes out of her kitchen and so happy I finally have her cookbook so I can recreate the meals in my home.

--Julianna Crowder, Leander, Texas
A GIrl and A Gun Club

CONTENTS:

CONTENTS

DEDICATION...1
AFFIRMATION...2
CONTENTS..4
CHEF PATRICIA CASHION..11
HEATHER TAYLOR, RDN, LDN..12
ALLERGENS..14
THE DIRTY DOZEN...15
THE CLEAN...15
RECIPE CHEF NOTES..17
    TIPS...17
    FLAVORS...17
TEMPERATURE AND SANITATION...18
    FOOD HANDLING AND STORAGE...18
    CLEANING YOUR VEGETABLES...18
THAWING...19
FIVE BASIC TASTES..20
    ADDITIONAL TASTE ADJUSTMENTS...21
    TIPS...21

RECIPES...23

BREAKFAST...25
Almond Flour Pancakes..27
Almond Pancakes (Egg Free)..28
Egg-Less Pancakes with Strawberry Rhubarb...30
Spinach Scramble...32
Turkey Ham Quiche in a Hash Brown Crust...34
Vegetable and Sausage Strata..37

BEEF...39
3 Meat Meatballs..40
Bacon Wrapped Beef Tenderloin Medallions..42
Beef and Broccoli Stir Fry...45
Beef Zucchini Enchiladas..46
Bison/Beef Chili...48
Bison Buffalo Joe..52
Country Fried Steak...54
Fruit Braised Lamb Shanks..56
Rosemary Flank Steak with Fig and Apple Chutney..................................60
Special Occasion Pot Roast..62
Sun-Dried Tomato Steak Spirals..64
Surf n' Turf Steak Topped with Grilled Shrimp.......................................66
Tex-Mex Ground Beef Sweet Potato Boats...68
Zest Beef Piccadilly...69

CHICKEN..71
Ancho-Chili Lime Glazed Chicken...72
Apple Chicken..75
Apricot Glazed Chicken..76
Orange-Cranberry Chicken with Toasted Walnuts....................................78
Rosemary Herb Chicken Bites..80
Seared Chicken in a Luscious Pomegranate Sauce....................................81
Spinach Stuffed Chicken Rolls...82

TURKEY...85
Caribbean Turkey Stew...86
Kale Turkey Burgers with Sun-Dried Tomato.......90
Roasted Turkey Legs with Cranberry-Jezebel Sauce...94
Sloppy Turkey..96
Turkey Walnut Romaine Tacos..............................98

PORK..101
BBQ Pork Square Ribs..103
Braised Pork Cutlets...104
Grilled Onion Pork Chops...................................106
Pork Chops with Blueberry Herb Sauce..............107
Pork Meatballs with Almond Bread Crumbs........109
"Red-Cooked" Pork and Vegetables.....................110
Savory Apple & Onion Pork Chops......................112
Spunky Asian Pork Meatballs..............................115

SEAFOOD...117
Crab Cakes..118
Cuban Halibut...120
Firecracker Mediterranean Salmon.....................123
Ginger-Dill Glazed Salmon.................................124
Grilled Tuna Steaks with Fresh Sweet Basil........126
Spicy Pineapple Glazed Cod Fillet......................127
Scallops and Vegetables over Zucchini Noodles....128
Sweet Potato Salmon Cakes................................130
Tuna, How to Cook..133

VEGGIE AND CASSEROLE......................................135
Chicken and Mushroom Casserole......................136
Easy Sweet Potato Veggie Burgers with Avocado...140
Mashed Creamy Squash & Kale Casserole..........142
Pesto Eggplant..145
Shepherds Cauliflower Mash Pie........................146
Zucchini Strip Lasagna.......................................148

DESSERT..151
Almond Honey Sop...152
Apple Crisp...152
Boiled Pineapple Rings.......................................154
Carrot Cake Treats..156
Fresh Berry Medley...158
Ginger Fruit Compote...159
No-Bake Cocoa Macaroons.................................161
Zucchini Crepes, Bacon Flavoed........................162

BREAD...165
Almond Bread...166
No Nut Bananad Bread..169

PIZZA..171
Acapulco Chicken Pizza......................................172
Almond Pizza Crust...174

PIZZA (continued)

Blueberry Tortilla Pizza..176
Chicago Style Pizza..177
Eggplant Pizza, No Crust...179
Fruit-E-Roni Pizza..180
Greek Inspired Pizza..181
Jerk Chicken, Pineapple & Canadian Bacon Pizza......................182
Portobello Mushroom & Pepper Pizza..................................183
Square Turkey Pizza...184
Veggie and Egg Pizza..187

TORTILLAS...189

Chipotle Lime Tortillas...190
Chips...190
Spinach and Kale Tortillas..193
Sun-Dried Tomato Basil Tortillas....................................194
Tomatillo Tortillas...197
Tortilla Base...198

FAT & OIL..201

Basil Oil...202
Clarified Butter..203
Flax Egg (Egg Replacement)..205

SEASONINGS...207

Allspice Seasoning..208
Anything Seasoning..209
Curry Powder..210
Five Spices Seasoning...211
Greek Seasoning...212
Italian Seasoning...213
Jamaican Jerk Seasoning...214
Lemon Pepper Seasoning..215
Montreal Seasoning..216
Poultry Seasoning...217
Sage Seasoning..218
Seasoning Salt..219
Steak Seasoning...220
Taco Seasoning..221

CONDIMENTS...223

Cashew Sour Cream...224
Clean Mayonnaise..225
Creamy Mustard Sauce..227
Dijon Mustard...228
Guacamole...230
Honey Cinnamon Almond Butter..233
Ketchup...234
Pickled Ginger..236
Roasted Garlic..238
Sour Cream..239
Toasted Nuts..241

CHUTNEY..243
Cranberry and Apricot Chutney..244
Fig and Apple Chutney...245
Honey Maple Chutney..246
Raspberry Honey Nut Chutney...247

SAUCES..249
Basic Tomato Sauce or **Pizza Sauce**....................................250
Basting Sauce...251
BBQ Sauce...252
Béarnaise Sauce..253
Bell Pepper, Garlic and Turkey Spaghetti Sauce..................254
Cherry Walnut Topping...256
Chili Sauce...257
Cilantro-Avocado Cream Sauce...258
Cranberry Sauce with Lime and Ginger................................260
Creamy Maple and Tahini Sauce..261
Enchilada Sauce..262
Ginger-Dill Glaze Sauce..263
Nightshade Free Tomato Sauce..264
Spicy Ginger Sauce...266
The Best Pesto Sauce..268
Taco Sauce...270
Tzatziki Sauce...271

SIDE DISH/APPETIZER..273
Acorn Squash with Pear Stuffing..274
Apple Stuffed Mushrooms...275
Apricot, Curry and Mustard Carrots.....................................276
Artichoke with Lemon Butter...277
Avocado Deviled Eggs...278
Bacon Braised Brussels Sprouts...280
Braised Green Cabbage..281
Breaded Zucchini Bites..282
Canadian Bacon and Tomato Potato Skin Strips.................284
Cauliflower Rice..286
Cauliflower Rice Pilaf..288
Coconut Creamed Potatoes and Tomatoes...........................290
Creamed Pearl Onions...292
Garlic Green Beans...294
Garlic Infused Artichokes...295
Gourmet Mushrooms...297
Mushrooms with Marsala Wine...298
Nightshade Free Potato Salad...300
Oriental Vegetables..302
Pear Cider Braised Kale...303
Roasted Asparagus..305
Roasted Garlic Mashed Potatoes and Parsnips....................306
Roasted Vegetable Medley...309
Spaghetti Squash...310
Spaghetti Squash with Walnut Herb Pesto...........................312

SIDE DISH/APPETIZER (continued)

Spinach and Artichoke Bake..314
Steamed California Blend..315
Vegetable Bolognese...318
Sweet Potato Fritters with Pistachio Pumpkin Crust...319
Wilted Chard Mix...320
Zucchini Noodles, How to Make..323

SOUP and SALAD..325
Apple and Walnut Tuna Salad..326
Baby Green Salad with Oranges and Olives...327
Caribbean Chicken Salad with Cashews...328
Creamy Ginger Carrot Soup...330
Free Range Chicken Salad...332
Mint-Citrus Salad...334
Spicy Beef and Carrot Sslsad..336
Spicy Ginger Kale Salad..338
Spicy Ginger Kale Salad with Portobello and Pine Nuts...................................340
Spring Vegetable Minestrone..342

NUTRITION EXTRAS...345
SHOOT FOR HEALTHY NUTRITION TIPS...346
   IMMUNE SUPPORT..346
   GUT SUPPORT...347
   DETOXIFICATION SUPPORT...348
      LIVER DETOXIFICATION CHART...350
NUTRIENT FUNCTIONS, DEFICIENCY AND SYMPTOMS.......................351
FOODS THAT FIGHT INFLAMMATION...354
NIGHTSHADES..355
MEASUREMENT CONVERSIONS, U.S.AND METRIC..............................356
INTERNAL COOKING TEMPERATURES..357
LIQUID COOKING TEMPERATURES...358
OIL SMOKING POINTS...359
   OIL TIPS...360
PRODUCT RECOMMENDATIONS...361
BUYING GUIDE for Healthier Choices...362
NOTES...364

CHEF PATRICIA CASHION

A high-honors graduate of Le Cordon Bleu College of Culinary Arts, Chef Patricia has a passion for creating cuisine that is full-flavored, and power-packed with nutrient-dense ingredients; designed to heal from the inside out. She has worked with leading registered dieticians, integrative medicine doctors and specialists to design menus built around specific diet restrictions and patient limitations. Partnered with Dr. Amy Myers, Austin UltraHealth, individuals began healing nationwide, with weekly meal delivery. The following publications have showcased Chef Patricia Cashion's work and lifestyle in the clean eating industry: *The Outdoor Channel*, Babes with Bullets video, *Naturally Fit* magazine, *The Paleo Miracle* book, and Gun Club of America, *Hot Brass* magazine.

Patricia comes from 3 generations of early chiropractic and holistic healers; the Milling and Brown families. The Brown Sanatorium in Cisco, Texas was well known statewide for their drugless healing obtained through hands-on treatments and nutrition. Both families played an active part in sustainable farming and ranching. Family land was used to grow crops and raise livestock that supplied all the wholesome food patients needed during their stay and throughout the healing process. People traveled great distances to stay at the sanatorium for treatment when medicine was limited and had no answers; a time when ailments and diseases had no other options. Patient treatment and nutrition increased patients' life spans. Thanks to my great-grandfather, Dr N.A. Brown and grandfather, Dr Hugh Chief Brown (aka Papa) for being an example for years to come and for instilling in me the need for drugless healing and proper nutrition.

Patricia enjoys her free time with family and friends in fitness, gardening, cooking, hunting, shooting and living an adventurous life. Patricia also donates her time as Secretary on the Board of Directors of *The Valkyrie Initiative*, a 501(c)3 nonprofit organization dedicated to helping the veterans, first responders, and their families with reintegration and decompression from downrange while encouraging the best use of the warrior mentality, skills and personality. AGOGE FUEL is an official sponsor. thevalkyrieinitiative.com

Join us as we provide education in nutrition through maximizing ingredients to *heal from the inside out.*

HEATHER TAYLOR, RDN, LDN

Heather Taylor, RDN, LDN is a licensed registered dietitian and owner of Eat Well and Beyond. She practices nutrition and lifestyle therapy with a focus in integrative and functional medicine approaches. She provides nutrition therapy for numerous medical conditions such as heart disease, diabetes, weight loss, food allergies and sensitivities, gutdsybiosis, and many other inflammatory diseases. She also provides supportive wellness nutrition therapy for children, adolescents, pregnant mothers, and anyone looking to improve their health and function at their optimal capacity. Heather's passion comes from a background of holistic healing practices instilled in her at a very young age. Her grandfather, who was a pioneer in chiropractic care, sparked the idea that the body has an innate ability to heal itself given the right environment and support it needs. She translated this idea into her passion for food as "medicine". She recognized how food and our relationship with food can truly transform a person's wellbeing and way of life.

Her mission is to utilize science-based evidence in the area of food and nutrition and translate it into terms to which anyone can understand and relate. Her consultations typically consist of a full health history review, body composition testing, food sensitivity testing, symptoms analysis, and analysis for further testing and supplement support, lab reviews, and one-on-one food and lifestyle planning. She believes that food and lifestyle goal planning is not one size fits all and requires full participation from the patient. She believes all her patients need to have foundational education and training to make better food and lifestyle choices. Her goal is for all of her patients to walk away, knowing WHY they are making the food and lifestyle choices in order to improve their health and wellbeing. Her food planning focuses on low inflammatory, low glycemic, Mediterranean-style whole foods and gut health. She has a unique style of practice that never leaves out the connection between mind-body-spirit/belief.

She believes that total wellbeing cannot focus on only one aspect of health, and the entirety of the individual must be addressed in order to provide the best supportive services to her patients. This is why she not only focuses on nutrition therapy but also lifestyle therapy which includes but is not limited to; diet, relationship with food, stress and sleep management, and progressive exercise goal planning. All of her patients will leave knowing more about how food influences their health, which foods are specifically right for that individual, how to plan and organize foods and lifestyle choices to better support health and wellbeing, and restore balance to the mind and body.

ALLERGENS

Additives

Artificial Sweeteners

Dairy

Gluten

Grains

Hydrogenated Oils

Legumes

Peanuts

Preservatives

Soy

Sugars

Sulfites

Synthetic By-Products

Always check your labels.

GMO's are Genetically Modified Organisms, or non-food items. There is an abundance of products on the market today containing GMO ingredients.

Please note there are hidden allergies disguised under various recognizable ingredients; sneaky marketing.

We strongly suggest you conduct further research on information relating to GMO consumption and your overall health.

A great place to find integrative and functional medicine doctors in your area is the Institute of Functional Medicine at *functionalmedicine.org*

Our recipes will not include the ingredients listed above. Any consumption of these ingredients will be determined by the specific products that you purchase.

Buy products containing real ingredients.

THE DIRTY DOZEN

These vegetables and fruits are **high in pesticides**. They are known to wreak havoc on our internal systems.

Apples
Celery
Cherry Tomatoes
Cucumbers
Grapes
Hot Peppers

Kale Collard Greens
Nectarines
Peaches
Snap Peas
Sweet Bell Peppers

THE CLEAN 15

These vegetables and fruits are known to have the **lowest pesticide load**, and are the safest of grown crops with the least amount of contamination.

Asparagus
Avocados
Cantaloupe
Cauliflower
Eggplant
Grapefruit
Kiwi
Mango

Onions
Papayas
Pineapple
Sweet Corn (*grain; do not eat*)
Sweet Peas, frozen
Sweet Potatoes

Information provided by EWG.org

RECIPE CHEF NOTES

It's all about making healthier choices, enjoying the food we eat, and knowing that the foods in this cookbook are healing our bodies from the inside out. Below you will find tips for general recipe tips, how to adjust basic tastes, temperature and sanitation, food handling and storage recommendations; preventing foodborne illnesses, proper food thawing methods and more. Be sure to read through and learn ways to integrate healthier choices into your cuisine. We wish you much success in your journey to become a healthier YOU!

Each recipe will list the hightest sources of nutrients for each dish, or target nutrients. Find these listed under *Target Source* after each recipe method.

Blessings and Health,

Patricia & Heather

TIPS

- The goal is to create dishes which retain the most nutrient value in purchase and during the cooking process; the way we cook our food matters for higher nutrient value and overall health.
- Each recipe will have its own individual tips, if specific to that recipe.
- **Prepping ahead is important to make the eating healthy lifestyle easier to stay consistent.**
- Create your own dishes by adding a different healthy fat, seasoning, condiment, chutney or sauce. All freshly prepared with recipes found witin the designated sections.
- Make **Nightshade Free** *BBQ Sauce*, *page 252* - use the Nightshade Free Tomato Sauce as a base, instead of using regular tomato sauce.
- When wilting leafy greens in a skillet, remember that more is better. One cup will be about ½ cup when it's wilted. Kale & Spinach have mega nutrition; eat up.
- Depending on the brand of coconut oil, there may be a coconut flavor added to your dishes.
- You can substitute coconut oil in any dish, although it is does not have a high-smoke point. If you use with high temperatures, it has the potential to release free radicals and acrolein in your dishes. *We do not want to create free radicals.* For more information on **Oil Smoke Points**, *page 359.* You may also replace beef/tallow, lard and clarified butter as high temperature cooking oils.
- Extra virgin olive oil is *not* high temperature oil.
- We do not always promote specific products, although we like to share products that we love and use regularly; they will be included in the recipes, if applicable. You can also find them listed in the back, under *Product Recommendations, page 361.*
- 1 tbsp of fresh herbs = 1 tsp of dried herbs

FLAVORS

Always taste, test and adjust to your desired flavor. Sometimes a little can go a long way.

The *Five Basic Tastes, page 20* will help you adjust any dish. Fix your dish with these helpful hints in balancing flavors.

TEMPERATURE AND SANITATION

In regards to contamination and sanitation, all fresh foods, raw or cooked, need to be placed in refrigeration within 4 hours, unless chilled or heated at the proper temperatures. If your food is not held at these temperatures, bacterial growth is possible on a higher scale.

COLD FOOD, holding temperature: **41° F or lower**
HOT FOOD, holding temperature: **135° F or higher**

Please refer to ***Internal Cooking Temperatures and Liquid Cooking Temperatures,*** *pages 357.*

Undercooking and overcooking food can change how our food should actually taste.

FOOD HANDLING AND STORAGE

Food handling & storage are very important aspects in the cooking process and in the prevention of food-borne illness.   Most often you cannot see, taste, or smell bacteria that cause foodborne illness.

A few things to keep you, your food and your kitchen safe:
- Be sure to Wash your hands and any food surfaces that will be used to prepare food; before, during and after handling food (raw or cooked).
- Always separate raw food from cooked food.
- Never use the same cutting board or utensils to prepare raw and uncooked food. You should always wash and sanitize your utensils and cutting boards in between differnet foods. Properly sanitized equipment is an essential 'best practice'.
- Always use a thermometer to measure the Internal Temperature of your meat. To determine whether your dish is cooked all the way through, measure it at the thickest part. ***Internal Cooking Temperatures*** can be found on recipe pages where they are applicable, or *page 359-360.*
- Any unused food ingredient or cooked ingredient should be placed in the refrigerator immediately after use to prevent any bacterial growth or the spread of foodborne illnesses. Please store in an airtight container.
- Consuming raw or undercooked food may increase your risk of food-borne illness. People at the most risk are children, the elderly, and persons with a weakened immune system.

CLEANING YOUR VEGETABLES

If you do not have the means to buy organic on The Dirty Dozen organic fruits and vegetables, be sure to use a vinegar and water wash (1:3). This will help to remove a majority of chemicals from the outer layer; peeling also helps.

THAWING

Refrigerator Thaw – the BEST way

o   Remove food from freezer and immediately place in your refrigerator.

o   For every 5 LBS, thaw time is 24 hours.

o   Defrosted Poultry, Fish, and ground Meat can be kept in the refrigerator for 1-2 days before cooking.

o   Defrosted Beef, Pork, Lamb or Veal can be kept in the refrigerator for 3 to 5 days before cooking.

o   These are suggested days in the refrigerator before the chance of food contamination. Always smell and check before preparing your dish.

o   You can also use these parameters to safely freee and refreeze your uncooked food.

Cold Water Thaw

o   Thaw your food in COLD water. NEVER thaw in warm/hot water. Warm/Hot water allows for your food to be heated to levels where bacteria growth begins to multiply.

o   Change your Cold water every 30 minutes to keep the water cold where bacteria growth will not begin.

o   Small packages thaw in about 1 hour or less.

o   Larger foods thaw at about 1 LB every 30 minutes.

o   Cook your food immediately.

o   Refreeze *only* thoroughly cooked food using this method.

Microwave Thaw – not recommended, use only as a last resort

o   Set microwave to 'Defrost' or '50 percent power'.

o   Make sure the outer edges ***do not*** cook while the remainder is frozen; tricky.

o   Separate any food that is in pieces during the defrosting cycle.

o   Cook your food immediately.

o   Refreeze *only* thoroughly cooked food using this method.

NEVER thaw your food sitting on the counter.
Temperatures of *40° F - 140° F are unsafe for bacteria breeding.*

FIVE BASIC TASTES

Taste is created by the sensation of smell, texture, and aroma. ***Taste, Test and Adjust*** your recipes for remarkable dishes.

LETS START with what each flavor expresses:

1. **Salty** – Tangy; taste buds are located at the front of your tongue
   a. Its presence can perk up the flavors of ingredients in the dish
   b. Provides a balance to sweet or acid flavors by decreasing the sourness of acid and increasing the sweetness of sugar
2. **Sour** – Acidic, Sharp and Tart; taste buds on the side of the tongue
3. **Sweetness** – Pleasant; taste buds are located at the front of your tongue
4. **Bitterness** – Unpleasant, Sharp and Disagreeable; taste buds are located in the back of the mouth
5. **Unami** – Earthy, Meaty, Savory; can depend on the amount of salt in the dish

To create healthy, great tasting cuisine, it's important to balance flavors. Who wants a dish that is too salty, too sour, or too sweet? Before serving a dish you are not satisfied with, use the following to balance your flavors and "fix" your dish.

Always begin with adding a little more of the most basic ingredient, and then a little of one of the useful adjustments below.

Taste, Test and Adjust after each alteration.

1. Too Salty
   a. Salty balances sweet flavors
   b. Recipe - balance with sweet, sour or fatty flavors
   c. Soup or sauce - add coconut sugar and a squeeze of lemon juice
   d. Sprinkle salt over your vegetables to draw out the natural water and flavors in the vegetables
2. Too Sweet
   a. Sweet balances salty flavors
   b. Recipe - balance with sour, salt, bitter, spicy or fatty flavors
   c. Soup or sauce - balance with salty and lemon juice
3. Too Sour
   a. Sour balances sweet or salty flavors
   b. Recipe - balance with sweet, salty, fatty or bitter flavors
   c. Soup or sauce - add a bit of salt and sugar flavor
   d. Sourness can reduce the amount of salt needed in your recipe

  e. Sour adds brightness to vegetables
  f. Sour keeps leafy greens and fruits from oxidizing. Wrap a piece of seran wrap tightly against food to create an addiitional seal, to prevent oxidizing, or browning.
  g. Sour stimulates salivation production

4. Too Bitter
  a. Balances sweet, salty or sour flavors
  b. Bitter is highly alkaline

5. Unami
  a. Be sure to add in small doses to begin; taste, test and adjust
  b. Great when added appropriately to all other senses
  c. Carries aroma qualities
  d. Add Coconut Aminos to help obtain the earthy, savory flavor; replace soy sauce with coocnut aminos

ADDITIONAL TASTE ADJUSTMENTS

These are not a part of the standard Five Basic Tastes, although definitely worth mentioning.

1. Fats
  a. Fats calm the flavor and add depth to your recipe; also adding richness
  b. Fats emulsify
  c. Balance with sour or increase your liquid to fix overly fat flavor

2. Pungent/Spicy – (ex. Garlic, Onions, Ginger, Hot Peppers, Mustard)
  a. Balnace with sweet, fat or sour flavor
  b. Adds a little spunk and intensity to your recipe
  c. If adding to a raw taste, use cautiously

3. Too Bland – add salt and/or herbs/seasonings
  a. Balance with salt, sweet or spicy flavors

Adjust your additions GRADUALLY, and stir well with each addition. Taste, Test and Adjust after each addition. Make the changes you need until your taste explode, as you desire. Remember, a little can go a long way, especially when adding salty or bitter flavors.

TIPS

- Follow your own flavor palate to cook the foods you love.
- Some dishes develop their flavor through preparation and need ingredients added early in the cooking process. Using dried herbs in the beginning of the cook process allows them to temper and become rich

RECIPES

BREAKFAST

ALMOND FLOUR PANCAKES

1 cup almond flour

1/2 cup organic applesauce

1 tbsp coconut flour

2 free-range eggs

1/4 cup water

1/4 tsp freshly grated nutmeg

1/4 tsp fine grain sea salt

2 tbsps coconut oil

1/2 cup fresh berry

Nutrition Facts

Serving Size 1 cake (169g)

Servings Per Container 3

Amount Per Serving

Calories 390	Calories from Fat 280

	% Daily Value*
Total Fat 31g	48%
Saturated Fat 10g	50%
Trans Fat 0g	
Cholesterol 145mg	48%
Sodium 260mg	11%
Total Carbohydrate 20g	7%
Dietary Fiber 6g	24%
Sugars 10g	
Protein 13g	

Vitamin A 4%	•	Vitamin C 40%
Calcium 10%	•	Iron 10%

*Percent Daily Values are based on a 2,000 calorie diet. Your daily values may be higher or lower depending on your calorie needs.

		Calories	2,000	2,500
Total Fat	Less than		65g	80g
Saturated Fat	Less than		20g	25g
Cholesterol	Less than		300mg	300mg
Sodium	Less than		2,400mg	2,400mg
Total Carbohydrate			300g	375g
Dietary Fiber			25g	30g

Calories per gram:
Fat 9 • Carbohydrate 4 • Protein 4

Combine the almond flour, applesauce, coconut flour, egg, water, nutmeg and sea salt in a medium bowl; mix well. The batter will appear a little thicker than a normal.Heat 1 tablespoon of coconut oil in a skillet over medium-low heat.

When skillet is hot, pour 1/4 cup of batter into the skillet and cook for 2-3 minutes, until bubbles begin to pop in the batter. Flip the pancake over; cook for an additional 1-2 minutes. Add more oil to the pan, as needed, and repeat with remaining batter. Top with fresh berry.

Tip
Fluffier pancakes: add an additional free-range egg or replace water with 1/4 cup soda water.

Servings: 3

Target source of Protein, Dietary Fiber, Dietary Fats, Vitamin B12, Vitamin C, Calcium, Iron, Magnesium

Supportive of Immune Health

ALMOND PANCAKES (EGG FREE)

1/2 cup almond flour or almond meal

1/4 cup flax meal; sprinkle

1/3 cup sifted coconut flour

1/4 tsp cream of tartar

1/2 tsp baking soda

1/4 tsp fine grain sea salt

1 tbsp maple syrup

2/3 cup warm coconut milk

1/2 tsp almond extract

1 tsp vanilla extract

2 tbsps extra virgin olive oil

Nutrition Facts

Serving Size 4oz (114g)
Servings Per Container 4

Amount Per Serving

Calories 190	Calories from Fat 100

	% Daily Value*
Total Fat 11g	**17%**
Saturated Fat 2g	**10%**
Trans Fat 0g	
Cholesterol 0mg	**0%**
Sodium 350mg	**15%**
Total Carbohydrate 17g	**6%**
Dietary Fiber 8g	**32%**
Sugars 6g	
Protein 6g	

Vitamin A 6%	•	Vitamin C 35%
Calcium 10%	•	Iron 8%

*Percent Daily Values are based on a 2,000 calorie diet. Your daily values may be higher or lower depending on your calorie needs.

	Calories	2,000	2,500
Total Fat	Less than	65g	80g
Saturated Fat	Less than	20g	25g
Cholesterol	Less than	300mg	300mg
Sodium	Less than	2,400mg	2,400mg
Total Carbohydrate		300g	375g
Dietary Fiber		25g	30g

Calories per gram
Fat 9 • Carbohydrate 4 • Protein 4

Choice of fruit: 1 cup fresh chopped strawberry, raspberry, blackberry, banana or blueberry.
Do not chop blueberry, unless you want a blue pancake.

Chop your fruit and place in the freezer for 30 minutes or longer.

Dry Ingredients: combine almond flour/meal, flax meal, coconut flour, cream of tartar, baking soda, and sea salt; mix well. *Wet Ingredients:* combine maple syrup, coconut milk, almond extract and vanilla extract; mix well.

Add wet to dry mixture, mix thoroughly and let sit for a few minutes. The batter should thicken as you mix; pourable. If mixture is too thick, add 1 tablespoon of coconut, at a time; mix well until you reach desired consistency. Add pureed fruit at this point; mix to incorporate.

Remove frozen fruit from the freezer. Fold in fresh frozen fruit or you can add in as a puree for overall flavoring.

Heat 2 tablespoons of oil in a skillet over medium heat. When bubbles pop from the oil, add 1/4 cup pancake batter. Cook pancakes on one side for 30 seconds - 1 minutes until bottom is solid, and then add chopped fruit; cook for an additional 2 minutes until the bottom is cooked through. Flip with a spatula and cook an additional 1-2 minutes. Use additional oil in between pancakes, as needed.

Top with choice of fruit, maple syrup or local raw honey.

Tips
Any fruit can be added. Keep frozen fruit frozen until recipe says to take them out of the freezer.

Save over ripped bananas and place in the blender to puree.

Servings: 4

Target source of Protein, Dietary Fiber, Dietary Fats, Calcium, Vitamin C, Vitamin B12, Magnesium, Manganese

Supportive of Immune Health

EGG-LESS PANCAKES

3 tbsps coconut oil, measured liquid

3 tbsps spring water or soda water

2 tsps baking soda

2 pureed banana

8 pureed organic strawberry

1 tsp pure vanilla extract

2 tsps ground cinnamon

1/2 tsp freshly grated nutmeg

1 1/2 cups almond meal

2 tsps pure almond extract

Nutrition Facts		
Serving Size 7oz (218g)		
Servings Per Container 10		
Amount Per Serving		
Calories 220	Calories from Fat 130	
		% Daily Value*
Total Fat 14g		22%
Saturated Fat 4.5g		23%
Trans Fat 0g		
Cholesterol 0mg		0%
Sodium 260mg		11%
Total Carbohydrate 22g		7%
Dietary Fiber 5g		20%
Sugars 12g		
Protein 5g		
Vitamin A 2%	•	Vitamin C 90%
Calcium 10%	•	Iron 6%

*Percent Daily Values are based on a 2,000 calorie diet. Your daily values may be higher or lower depending on your calorie needs.

	Calories	2,000	2,500
Total Fat	Less than	65g	80g
Saturated Fat	Less than	20g	25g
Cholesterol	Less than	300mg	300mg
Sodium	Less than	2,400mg	2,400mg
Total Carbohydrate		300g	375g
Dietary Fiber		25g	30g

Calories per gram:
Fat 9 • Carbohydrate 4 • Protein 4

Preheat oven to 350° F.

In a food processor, combine oil, spring water, and baking soda. Add banana and strawberry; puree. Add vanilla extract, cinnamon, nutmeg, almond meal, and almond extract; mix well. Add more water if necessary, for desired consistency.

Spray a sheet pan with cooking spray. Spread out about 1/4 cup into a pancake shape and cook in the oven for 10-12 minutes. Pancakes will be a thin crepe consistency. When the pancake begins browning on edges, flip and cook for an additional 2-3 minutes. If they are not cooked through, they will tear. Use a fish spatula to carefully remove them. Add 1 tablespoon of water if batter thickens up. Times may vary, depending on thickness of your pancakes. Watch carefully.

Add fruit when pancakes begin to set up a little in the oven; at about 5-7 minutes.

with STRAWBERRY RHUBARB SAUCE

SAUCE

6 cups fresh rhubarb

1 1/2 cups organic applesauce

1/2 tsp lemon zest

1/4 tsp ground ginger

1 cinnamon stick or 1 tbsp ground cinnamon

2 cups halved fresh organic strawberry

1 tablespoon of oil

Combine all ingredients, except strawberry; mix well. Heat 1 tablespoon of oil over medium-low heat.

Reduce the heat to low when all ingredients are incorporated. Cover with a lid and sauté for 30 minutes; stirring occasionally. Add strawberry the last 7 minutes of cook time.

Yield: 10 pancakes

Target source of Protein, Dietary Fiber, Dietary Fats, Vitamin K, Vitamin C, Calcium, Magnesium, Manganese, Potassium

Supportive of Immune Health

SPINACH SCRAMBLE

6 free-range egg whites

1 free-range egg yolk

1/2 tbsp chopped fresh oregano or 1/2 tsp dried oregano

1/2 tsp ground paprika

1 tsp coconut oil, measured melted

1 diced zucchini, about 3/4 cup

1 minced organic red bell pepper, seeds and ribs removed

1 chopped organic plum tomato

1 cup organic spinach with stem, lightly packed

Nutrition Facts

Serving Size 1 1/2 cup (292g)
Servings Per Container 2

Amount Per Serving

Calories 140	Calories from Fat 45

	% Daily Value^
Total Fat 5g	8%
Saturated Fat 3g	15%
Trans Fat 0g	
Cholesterol 90mg	30%
Sodium 190mg	8%
Total Carbohydrate 9g	3%
Dietary Fiber 3g	12%
Sugars 5g	
Protein 14g	

Vitamin A 70%	•	Vitamin C 120%
Calcium 6%	•	Iron 8%

*Percent Daily Values are based on a 2,000 calorie diet. Your daily values may be higher or lower depending on your calorie needs.

		Calories	2,000	2,500
Total Fat	Less than		65g	80g
Saturated Fat	Less than		20g	25g
Cholesterol	Less than		300mg	300mg
Sodium	Less than		2,400mg	2,400mg
Total Carbohydrate			300g	375g
Dietary Fiber			25g	30g

Calories per gram:
Fat 9 • Carbohydrate 4 • Protein 4

Whisk egg whites, egg yolk, oregano, paprika and set aside.

Heat the oil in a large skillet over medium-high heat. Add zucchini, bell pepper and tomato; sauté until vegetables soften and begin to brown, about 3 minutes. Stir often.

Slowly pour in the egg mixture; sauté for about 3 minutes, stirring constantly until eggs are cooked through.

Servings: 2

Target source of Protein, Vitamin A, Vitamins B2, B6, Folate, Vitamin C, Vitamin K, Iodine, Selenium, Manganese, Magnesium, Potassium, Phosphorus, Molybdenum

Supportive of Immune and Detoxification Health

TURKEY HAM QUICHE IN A HASH BROWN CRUST

3 cups grated organic Yukon gold potato

1/2 cup chopped sweet onion, divided

2 tbsps chopped organic green bell pepper

Dash of ground white pepper

1 free-range egg, beaten

1 1/2 cups pastured, uncured diced turkey ham; about 12 oz

1/4 cup chopped sweet onion

1/2 cup coconut milk

4 free-range eggs

2 tsps Dijon Mustard, page 228

1/4 tsp ground white pepper

Nutrition Facts		
Serving Size 1 slice (170g)		
Servings Per Container 6		
Amount Per Serving		
Calories 210	Calories from Fat 100	
		% Daily Value*
Total Fat 11g		17%
Saturated Fat 5g		25%
Trans Fat 0g		
Cholesterol 215mg		72%
Sodium 690mg		29%
Total Carbohydrate 10g		3%
Dietary Fiber 1g		4%
Sugars 3g		
Protein 16g		
Vitamin A 6%	•	Vitamin C 10%
Calcium 2%	•	Iron 10%

*Percent Daily Values are based on a 2,000 calorie diet. Your daily values may be higher or lower depending on your calorie needs.

	Calories	2,000	2,500
Total Fat	Less than	65g	80g
Saturated Fat	Less than	20g	25g
Cholesterol	Less than	300mg	300mg
Sodium	Less than	2,400mg	2,400mg
Total Carbohydrate		300g	375g
Dietary Fiber		25g	30g

Calories per gram:
Fat 9 • Carbohydrate 4 • Protein 4

Preheat oven to 400° F.

Prepare Dijon Mustard.

CRUST

Combine potato, 1/4 cup onion, bell pepper and dash of white pepper. Fold in 1 beaten egg. In a 9-inch pie pan, spray cooking oil to coat. Spray.

To form the crust, carefully pat down potato mixture evenly into pie pan, building up sides for rim. Bake crust in the oven for 25 to 30 minutes until golden brown. Turn off oven heat and allow crust to cool.

NOTE: Recipe may be prepared up to this point, cooled, covered and refrigerated until ready to serve. ***To reheat:*** Place crust in the cold oven. Heat the oven to 275° F and heat crust for 10 minutes. Remove the crust from the oven and continue with following steps.

FILLING

Sprinkle turkey ham and remaining 1/4 cup onion, in layers evenly over crust. Combine coconut milk, four eggs, mustard, and 1/4 tsp white pepper; mix well. Pour over ingredients in crust.

Bake for 30-35 minutes until a toothpick comes out clean. Let stand 5 minutes before cutting.

Servings: 6

Target source of Protein, Dietary Fats, Omega 3 Fat, Vitamin B12, Vitamin C, Manganese, Potassium, Iron

Supportive of Immune Health

VEGETABLE AND SAUSAGE STRATA

5 cups Almond Bread Crumbs, page 166

8 ozs cooked pastured, uncured smoked sausage links, cut into
   1/2-inch pieces

2/3 cup sliced mushroom

1/2 cup chopped organic green bell pepper

4 free-range eggs, beaten

1 3/4 cups coconut milk

1 tbsp snipped chive

1 tbsp snipped fresh oregano or 1 tsp crushed dried oregano

1/4 tsp fine grain sea salt

1/8 tsp ground black pepper

Nutrition Facts

Serving Size 4 oz (169g)
Servings Per Container 12

Amount Per Serving

Calories 460	Calories from Fat 340

	% Daily Value*
Total Fat 38g	58%
Saturated Fat 12g	60%
Trans Fat 0g	
Cholesterol 250mg	83%
Sodium 770mg	32%
Total Carbohydrate 16g	5%
Dietary Fiber 6g	24%
Sugars 7g	
Protein 17g	

Vitamin A 8%	•	Vitamin C 10%	
Calcium 10%	•	Iron 20%	

*Percent Daily Values are based on a 2,000 calorie diet. Your daily values may be higher or lower depending on your calorie needs.

	Calories	2,000	2,500
Total Fat	Less than	65g	80g
Saturated Fat	Less than	20g	25g
Cholesterol	Less than	300mg	300mg
Sodium	Less than	2,400mg	2,400mg
Total Carbohydrate		300g	375g
Dietary Fiber		25g	30g

Calories per gram:
Fat 9 • Carbohydrate 4 • Protein 4

Preheat oven to 325° F.

Prepare Almond Bread; crumb.

Spray two square 8-inch baking dishes with cooking oil. Divide the cubed bread crumbs in half and layer into both baking dishes evenly. Top with sausage, mushroom and bell pepper. Place any remaining bread cubes on top.

Combine eggs, milk, chive, oregano, sea salt, and black pepper; mix well. Pour the mixture evenly between the two baking dishes, cover and refrigerate for 1 hour.

Bake uncovered for 40 to 45 minutes until a toothpick comes out clean. Let stand 10 minutes before serving.

Servings: 12

Target source of Protein, Dietary Fiber, Dietary Fats, Vitamin B12, Iron, Calcium, Magnesium, Manganese

Supportive of Immune Health

BEEF

3 MEAT MEATBALLS

2 lbs grass-fed ground beef or 93/7 lean ground beef

2 lb pastured, uncured ground pork

3/4 cup finely diced pastured, uncured Canadian bacon

1/2 cup chopped onion

6 tbsps organic applesauce

1/4 cup almond meal

1/4 tsp fine grain sea salt and

1/4 tsp ground black pepper

1 1/2 tbsps fresh chopped oregano or 4 tsps dried oregano

1 cup Nightshade Free Tomato Sauce, page 264

Nutrition Facts		
Serving Size 6oz (224g)		
Servings Per Container 8		
Amount Per Serving		
Calories 350	Calories from Fat 180	
		% Daily Value*
Total Fat 20g		31%
Saturated Fat 7g		35%
Trans Fat 0g		
Cholesterol 115mg		38%
Sodium 460mg		19%
Total Carbohydrate 4g		1%
Dietary Fiber 1g		4%
Sugars 2g		
Protein 37g		
Vitamin A 0%	•	Vitamin C 15%
Calcium 2%	•	Iron 15%

*Percent Daily Values are based on a 2,000 calorie diet. Your daily values may be higher or lower depending on your calorie needs.

		Calories:	2,000	2,800
Total Fat	Less than		65g	80g
Saturated Fat	Less than		20g	25g
Cholesterol	Less than		300mg	300mg
Sodium	Less than		2,400mg	2,400mg
Total Carbohydrate			300g	375g
Dietary Fiber			25g	30g

Calories per gram:
Fat 9 • Carbohydrate 4 • Protein 4

Preheat oven to 350° F.

Prepare Nightshade Free Tomato Sauce.

Combine all ingredients in a large bowl; mix well and shape into 1 ounce balls. Place on a lightly sprayed sheet pan. Bake for 20-30 minutes. Internal temperature should read 160° F, at the thickest part; no pink inside.

Top with Nightshade Free Tomato Sauce.

Servings: 4

Target source of Protein, Vitamins B3, B12, Zinc, Saturated Fats

Supportive of Immune Health

41.

BACON WRAPPED BEEF TENDERLOIN MEDALLIONS

4 grass-fed chuck beef steak, cut into medallions

8 pastured, uncured bacon slices

8 toothpicks, 2 per medallion

1/4 cup Steak Seasoning, page 220

1/4-1/2 tbsp fine grain sea salt

2 tbsps extra virgin olive oil, more as needed

Nutrition Facts

Serving Size 6 oz (179g)
Servings Per Container 4

Amount Per Serving

Calories 360   Calories from Fat 180

	% Daily Value*
Total Fat 21g	32%
Saturated Fat 6g	30%
Trans Fat 0g	
Cholesterol 115mg	38%
Sodium 2270mg	95%
Total Carbohydrate 0g	0%
Dietary Fiber 0g	0%
Sugars 0g	
Protein 46g	

Vitamin A 0%	Vitamin C 0%
Calcium 2%	Iron 25%

*Percent Daily Values are based on a 2,000 calorie diet. Your daily values may be higher or lower depending on your calorie needs.

	Calories	2,000	2,500
Total Fat	Less than	65g	80g
Saturated Fat	Less than	20g	25g
Cholesterol	Less than	300mg	300mg
Sodium	Less than	2,400mg	2,400mg
Total Carbohydrate		300g	375g
Dietary Fiber		25g	30g

Calories per gram
Fat 9 • Carbohydrate 4 • Protein 4

Preheat oven to 350° F.

Prepare Steak Seasoning.

Cut steak into 3 ounce medallions. Wrap 2 bacon slices around raw medallion securing with a toothpick where bacon ends come together. Season each side of steak with steak seasoning and sea salt. Brush cooking oil on both sides of the medallion.

Heat the oil in the skillet over medium-high heat. Sear steaks on both sides and around bacon covered edges until brown, about 2-3 minutes. Place steaks on a baking sheet pan and bake for about 13 minutes. Internal temperature for beef, should read 160° F, at the thickest part.

Remove from oven and make a tent cover with aluminum foil; rest 5-7 minutes to allow steak to finish cooking.

Tips
These juicy mini-steaks are packed with protein.

Look for beef with the lowest fat marbeling, if your not buying grass-fed beef.

Servings: 4

Target source of Protein, Dietary Fats, Iron, B Vitamins, Zinc, Selenium, Phosphorus, Potassium

Supportive of Immune and Detoxification Health

BEEF & BROCCOLI STIR FRY

1 1/2 lbs grass-fed flank steak, or lean flank steak Milanese,
   cut into strips
1/2 tsp Five Spices Seasoning, page 211
4 cups grated Cauliflower Rice, page 286
1/2 tsp fine grain sea salt
1/2 tsp ground black pepper
2 tbsps extra virgin olive oil
1 1/4 cups broccoli florets, with stem
2 tsps minced fresh ginger root
1 crushed garlic clove
1 tsp coconut sugar
1 tbsp coconut aminos
2 tbsps organic beef broth
5 tbsps sliced raw almond

Nutrition Facts		
Serving Size 1 3/4 cups (439g)		
Servings Per Container 4		
Amount Per Serving		
Calories 570	Calories from Fat 290	
		% Daily Value*
Total Fat 32g		49%
Saturated Fat 11g		55%
Trans Fat 0g		
Cholesterol 155mg		52%
Sodium 550mg		23%
Total Carbohydrate 16g		5%
Dietary Fiber 6g		24%
Sugars 5g		
Protein 54g		
Vitamin A 20%	•	Vitamin C 200%
Calcium 10%	•	Iron 25%
*Percent Daily Values are based on a 2,000 calorie diet. Your daily values may be higher or lower depending on your calorie needs.		

		Calories	2,000	2,500
Total Fat	Less than		65g	80g
Saturated Fat	Less than		20g	25g
Cholesterol	Less than		300mg	300mg
Sodium	Less than		2,400mg	2,400mg
Total Carbohydrate			300g	375g
Dietary Fiber			25g	30g

Calories per gram:
Fat 9 • Carbohydrate 4 • Protein 4

Prepare Five Spices Seasoning and Cauliflower Rice.

Sprinkle sea salt, black pepper and five spice seasoning over flank steak on both sides. Cut into strips along the grain.

Heat the oil in a large skillet or wok over high heat. Add flank steak and cook for 3 minutes; barely pink, stirring often. Add broccoli, ginger root, garlic, coconut sugar, coconut aminos and beef broth; sauté about 7-10 minutes until vegetables are crisp tender. Remove meat with tongs, if it begins to look overcook. Add almonds at the last two minutes of cook time.

Tip
(1:1) oil to coconut aminos; mix well. Serve on the side for dipping. Add a small bit at a time to final dish, if you prefer more sauce.

Servings: 4

Target source of Protein, Dietary Fats, Vitamin A, Vitamin C, B Vitamins, Folate, Vitamin K, Pentothentic Acid, Iron, Manganese, Phosphorus, Potassium, Selerium, Zinc,

Supportive of Immune Health

BEEF-ZUCCHINI ENCHILADAS

12-15 Chipotle-Lime Tortilla, page 190

1 thinly sliced variety organic bell pepper

1 thinly sliced sweet onion

2 lbs grass-fed ground beef or 93/7 lean ground beef

1 tbsp coconut oil, measured solid

1 minced garlic clove

1 cup Enchilada Sauce, page 262

1 cup diced organic tomato

1 tbsp organic chili powder

1 tbsp local raw honey

2 tbsps chopped fresh basil or 2 tsps dried basil

1 tsp ground cumin

1 tsp ground organic cayenne

1 bay leaf

1/4 tsp fine grain sea salt

1/8 tsp ground black pepper

2 cups shredded zucchini

1 sliced organic black olives, drained, 4 oz can

1/2 cup Enchilada Sauce, page 262

1/4 cup minced fresh cilantro, garnish

1/2 tsp fine grain sea salt, garnish

Nutrition Facts

Serving Size 2 enciladas (579g)
Servings Per Container 6

Amount Per Serving

Calories 640   Calories from Fat 310

	% Daily Value^
Total Fat 35g	54%
Saturated Fat 10g	50%
Trans Fat 0.5g	
Cholesterol 475mg	158%
Sodium 3220mg	134%
Total Carbohydrate 26g	9%
Dietary Fiber 8g	32%
Sugars 11g	
Protein 56g	

Vitamin A 30%	•	Vitamin C 70%
Calcium 15%	•	Iron 40%

*Percent Daily Values are based on a 2,000 calorie diet. Your daily values may be higher or lower depending on your calorie needs.

	Calories	2,000	2,500
Total Fat	Less than	65g	80g
Saturated Fat	Less than	20g	25g
Cholesterol	Less than	300mg	300mg
Sodium	Less than	2,400mg	2,400mg
Total Carbohydrate		300g	375g
Dietary Fiber		25g	30g

Calories per gram:
Fat 9 • Carbohydrate 4 • Protein 4

Preheat oven to 350° F.

Prepare Chipotle-Lime Tortilla (3 batches) and Enchila Sauce.

Heat the oil in a large skillet over medium-high heat. Add bell pepper and onion; sauté for 2 minutes. Add beef; sauté about 5 minutes; no pink. Add garlic; sauté an additional 1 minute.

Stir in enchilada sauce, tomato, chili powder, honey, basil, cumin, cayenne, bay leaf, sea salt and black pepper. Bring the skillet to a boil over medium-high heat; reduce and simmer for 10-15 minutes or until slightly thickened. Add zucchini and olive; sauté for 5 minutes, until crisp tender. Discard bay leaf from saucepan. Remove mixture from heat.

Take one prepared tortilla and fill with mixture. Roll and carefully place tortillas in two baking dishes sprayed with cooking oil. Line in a single row; repeat the process with remaining ingredients; reserve some to spread on top.

Spread remaining enchilada sauce and reserved mixture on top of enchiladas. Bake uncovered for 20 minutes. Remove from heat and sprinkle with cilantro and sea salt.

Tip
Double the recipe to freeze ahead. Enchilada Sauce is grat to prep ahead and freeze.

Servings: 6

Target source of Protein, Dietary Fats, Vitamins B3, B6, B12, Vitamin C, Phosphorus, Potassium, Selenium, Zinc

Supportive of Immune Health

BISON/BEEF CHILI

3 lbs ground bison, 3 lbs grass-fed OR 93/7 lean ground beef

1 1/2 tbsps extra virgin olive oil

1 cup finely chopped sweet onion

1/2 tsp fine grain sea salt

1/4 tsp ground black pepper

2 diced organic jalapeno chilies, stems and seeds removed

1 cup diced organic celery

1 cup diced organic red bell pepper

4 cups diced organic tomato, peeled and seeded

6 tbsps organic tomato paste

1 cup organic vegetable broth

4 minced garlic clove

2 tbsps organic chili powder

2 tsps ground cumin

1 tbsp chopped fresh oregano or 1 tsp dried oregano

Pinch of fine grain sea salt & ground black pepper

1/4 tsp ground organic cayenne pepper

1 tsp original Tabasco hot sauce

1/2 cup chopped green onion, garnish

1/4 cup fresh cilantro or 4 tsps dried cilantro, garnish

3/4 cup Sour Cream, page 239

Nutrition Facts

Serving Size 7oz (416g)
Servings Per Container 8

Amount Per Serving

Calories 340 — Calories from Fat 140

% Daily Value^

Total Fat 15g — 23%
Saturated Fat 5g — 25%
Trans Fat 0g

Cholesterol 95mg — 32%

Sodium 630mg — 26%

Total Carbohydrate 15g — 5%
Dietary Fiber 3g — 12%
Sugars 7g

Protein 37g

Vitamin A 25% • Vitamin C 90%

Calcium 10% • Iron 35%

*Percent Daily Values are based on a 2,000 calorie diet. Your daily values may be higher or lower depending on your calorie needs.

	Calories:	2,000	2,500
Total Fat	Less than	65g	80g
Saturated Fat	Less than	20g	25g
Cholesterol	Less than	300mg	300mg
Sodium	Less than	2,400mg	2,400mg
Total Carbohydrate		300g	375g
Dietary Fiber		25g	30g

Calories per gram:
Fat 9 • Carbohydrate 4 • Protein 4

Prepare Sour Cream, optional.

Heat a skillet over medium-high heat. Add the beef; sauté until cooked through, no pink. Strain grease and discard fat.

Heat the oil in a large saucepan over medium heat. Add onion, and a pinch each of sea salt and black pepper; sauté for about 5 minutes until softened.

Add the jalapeño, celery and bell pepper; sauté for 5-7 minutes, until softened. Add tomato, tomato paste and broth; mix well to incorporate.

Increase the heat to medium-high. Add the garlic, chili powder, cumin, oregano, sea salt, black pepper, cayenne and hot sauce; simmer for about 10-15 minutes until mixture is thickened.

Garnish with chopped green onions, fresh chopped cilantro and sour cream.

Servings: 4

Target source of Vitamins B12, B6, B3, Vitamin A, Vitamin C

Supportive of Immune, Gut and Neurological Health

BISON BUFFALO JOE

1/2 lb ground bison

2 minced garlic clove

1 shredded organic carrot, peeled

3 cups roughly chopped organic baby spinach

1 cup diced organic tomato

2 tsps Dijon Mustard, page 228

2 tsps Mother's apple cider vinegar

1 tsp maple syrup, grade B

1/4 cup chopped green onion

Sliced avocado, garnish

Nutrition Facts

Serving Size 3/4 cup (193g)
Servings Per Container 4

Amount Per Serving	
Calories 120	Calories from Fat 35

	% Daily Value*
Total Fat 4g	6%
Saturated Fat 1.5g	8%
Trans Fat 0g	
Cholesterol 30mg	10%
Sodium 210mg	9%
Total Carbohydrate 8g	3%
Dietary Fiber 2g	8%
Sugars 4g	
Protein 13g	

Vitamin A 120%	•	Vitamin C 40%
Calcium 8%	•	Iron 20%

*Percent Daily Values are based on a 2,000 calorie diet. Your daily values may be higher or lower depending on your calorie needs.

	Calories	2,000	2,500
Total Fat	Less than	65g	80g
Saturated Fat	Less than	20g	25g
Cholesterol	Less than	300mg	300mg
Sodium	Less than	2,400mg	2,400mg
Total Carbohydrate		300g	375g
Dietary Fiber		25g	30g

Calories per gram:
Fat 9 • Carbohydrate 4 • Protein 4

Prepare Dijon Mustard.

Heat a large skillet with a tight-fitting lid on medium-high. Gradually add bison a bit at a time and cook, stirring frequently and breaking up bison meat with a wooden spoon, until browned, about 3 minutes; no pink

Add garlic, carrot and spinach to the skillet; stir occasionally until spinach wilts, about 3 minute. Stir in tomato, mustard, vinegar and maple syrup. Cover pan, reduce heat to medium and simmer; stirring occasionally, until cooked through but still moist and saucy, about 8-10 minutes. Add green onion; toss to combine. Garnish with sliced avocado.

Tip
You can substitute any grass-fed beef or any lean meat.

Servings: 4

Target source of Protein, Omega 3, Vitamin A, Vitamin C, Vitamin K, Vitamins B1, B2, B3, B6, B12, Folate, Iron, Magnesium, Manganese, Phosphorus, Potassium, Selenium, Zinc

Supportive of Immune and Detoxification Health

COUNTRY FRIED STEAK

4 grass-fed cubed steaks

4 free-range eggs, beaten

1/2 cup almond meal, more as needed

1/8 cup sifted coconut flour

1 tsp garlic powder

1 tsp fine grain sea salt

1 tsp ground black pepper

1/2 cup Clarified Butter, page 203

3 tbsps extra virgin olive oil, more as needed

Nutrition Facts		
Serving Size 1 steak (236g)		
Servings Per Container 4		
Amount Per Serving		
Calories 980	Calories from Fat 820	
		% Daily Value*
Total Fat 91g		140%
Saturated Fat 36g		180%
Trans Fat 4g		
Cholesterol 380mg		127%
Sodium 730mg		30%
Total Carbohydrate 10g		3%
Dietary Fiber 4g		16%
Sugars 2g		
Protein 31g		
Vitamin A 25%	• Vitamin C 0%	
Calcium 10%	• Iron 20%	

*Percent Daily Values are based on a 2,000 calorie diet. Your daily values may be higher or lower depending on your calorie needs.

	Calories	2,000	2,500
Total Fat	Less than	65g	80g
Saturated Fat	Less than	20g	25g
Cholesterol	Less than	300mg	300mg
Sodium	Less than	2,400mg	2,400mg
Total Carbohydrate		300g	375g
Dietary Fiber		25g	30g

Calories per gram:
Fat 9 • Carbohydrate 4 • Protein 4

Prepare Clarified Butter.

Beat the egg and place on a plate for dredging. Combine almond meal, coconut flour, garlic powder, sea salt and black pepper; mix well and place on another plate to dredge.

Dip each steak into the egg mixture and then into the dry ingredients. Repeat a second time for full coverage.

Heat clarified butter and oil in a skillet over medium-high heat. When oil is hot, place the steak in the skillet; fry for 3 minutes. Add extra oil as needed. Carefully flip steak and cook for another 3 minutes. Flip again until all pink in meat is cooked through. Internal temperature should read, 160° F, at the thickest part.

Tips
If you cannot have egg, you can replace with a little coconut milk and soak for 30 minutes before dredging in almond meal; flax egg substitute will not work here.

The key to a good frying is keeping plenty of clean frying liquid in the skillet.

Servings: 4

Target source of Protein, Dietary Fats, Vitamins B2, B3, B12, Iron, Calcium, Magnesium, Phosphorus, Potassium, Zinc

Supportive of Immune Health

FRUIT-BRAISED LAMB SHANKS

3 lbs grass-fed lamb shanks or lean lamb shanks

1 tbsp Clarified Butter, page 203

1 tbsp extra virgin olive oil

1/2 cup minced onion

1 minced garlic clove

1 bay leaf

1 tbsp chopped fresh thyme or 1 tsp dried thyme

1 tbsp almond flour; sprinkled

1 tbsp turmeric

1/2 tsp dried organic chili flake

2 cups organic chicken broth

3/4 cup dry white wine

2 chopped peach, peeled

2 chopped nectarine, peeled

2 chopped organic plum, skin on

Nutrition Facts
Serving Size 5 oz piece (11 oz total weight) (328g)
Servings Per Container 8

Amount Per Serving

Calories 340   Calories from Fat 110

% Daily Value*

Total Fat 12g — 18%
Saturated Fat 4g — 20%
Trans Fat 0g
Cholesterol 135mg — 45%
Sodium 330mg — 14%
Total Carbohydrate 12g — 4%
Dietary Fiber 2g — 8%
Sugars 8g
Protein 41g

Vitamin A 8% • Vitamin C 10%
Calcium 4% • Iron 20%

*Percent Daily Values are based on a 2,000 calorie diet. Your daily values may be higher or lower depending on your calorie needs.

	Calories	2,000	2,500
Total Fat	Less than	65g	80g
Saturated Fat	Less than	20g	25g
Cholesterol	Less than	300mg	300mg
Sodium	Less than	2,400mg	2,400mg
Total Carbohydrate		300g	375g
Dietary Fiber		25g	30g

Calories per gram:
Fat 9 • Carbohydrate 4 • Protein 4

Prepare Clarified Butter.

Melt the clarified butter in a skillet over medium heat, and add the oil. Add the shanks and sauté them for 3-4 minutes on each side. Internal temperature should read 160° F, at the thickest part. Remove the shanks and set aside. Discard all but 2 tablespoon of fat from the pan. Scrape bits on the bottom of the skillet.

Add onion and garlic; sauté 1-2 minutes. Add the bay leaf, thyme, turmeric, chili flakes and sprinkle the almond flour; sauté for 1-2 minutes, and then add the dry wine. Add 1 1/2 cups of the chicken broth. Return the shanks to the pan. Reduce the heat to low and cover; simmer for 1 1/2 hours.

Add the fruit and continue to cook an additional 45 minutes until the meat is tender and can be pulled away from the bone. Stir occasionally while cooking, basting the shanks with the sauce.

As the sugar in the fruit begins to stick, stir more frequently; sauce will thicken. If sauce is too thick, add a little more broth a little at a time. If at any time you add too much liquid, turn up the heat a bit and allow the sauce to reduce; stirring occasionally. When the shanks are done, remove them from the pan and pull away the meat; reserve bones for the homemade lamb broth or to feed to the dogs. Skim the surface fat from the sauce.

Return the pulled meat to the sauce and cook over low heat for 3 to 4 minutes, to heat through. Serve immediately.

Servings: 5

Target source of Protein, Dietary Fats, Vitamins B1, B2, B3, B6, B12, Pantothenic Acid, Copper, Phosphorus, Iron, Potassium, Selenium, Magnesium, Zinc

Supportive of Immune Health

ROSEMARY FLANK STEAK WITH FIG AND APPLE CHUTNEY

1 tbsp chopped fresh rosemary or 1 tsp dried rosemary

2 minced garlic clove

3/4 tsp fine grain sea salt

1/2 tsp ground black pepper

1 tbsp extra virgin olive oil

2 1/4 lbs grass-fed flank steak or lean flank steak; Milanese

2 cups Fig and Apple Chutney, page 245

2 tbsps chopped parsley, garnish

Nutrition Facts

Serving Size (407g)
Servings Per Container 8

Amount Per Serving

Calories 540	Calories from Fat 210

	% Daily Value*
Total Fat 24g	37%
Saturated Fat 9g	45%
Trans Fat 0g	
Cholesterol 95mg	32%
Sodium 850mg	35%
Total Carbohydrate 47g	16%
Dietary Fiber 1g	4%
Sugars 31g	
Protein 37g	

Vitamin A 8%	•	Vitamin C 35%
Calcium 2%	•	Iron 30%

*Percent Daily Values are based on a 2,000 calorie diet. Your daily values may be higher or lower depending on your calorie needs.

	Calories	2,000	2,500
Total Fat	Less than	65g	80g
Saturated Fat	Less than	20g	25g
Cholesterol	Less than	300mg	300mg
Sodium	Less than	2,400mg	2,400mg
Total Carbohydrate		300g	375g
Dietary Fiber		25g	30g

Calories per gram
Fat 9 • Carbohydrate 4 • Protein 4

Prepare Fig and Apple Chutney.

In a small bowl, add rosemary, garlic, sea salt, black pepper and 1 tablespoon of oil; mix well.

Heat 2 tablespoons of oil in a skillet over medium-high heat. When the pan is very hot, add the steak; sauté for 3 minutes on both sides. Internal temperature should read, 160° F, at the thickest part. Let stand 5 minutes.

Top with fig and apple chutney. Garnish with parsley.

Tips
Flank steak can also be referred to as Milanese.

This steak is very thin and will cook fast. If over cooked, it can become rubbery.

Servings: 6

Target source of Protein, Dietary Fats, Vitamin B12, Vitamin C, Vitamin K, Copper, Selenium, Phosphorus, Potassium, Zinc

Supportive of Immune Health

SPECIAL OCCASION POT ROAST

2 lbs grass-fed chuck roast or lean chuck roast, trim fat; cut
  into 2-inch cubes

1 tsp fine grain sea salt

1 tsp ground black pepper

2 tsps ground cumin

3 1/2 tbsps extra virgin olive oil, divided

1 cup chopped white onion

6 chopped garlic clove

1 cup organic tomato juice

1/3 cup balsamic vinegar

1 cup chopped organic black olives

1/2 cup dark or golden raisins

Nutrition Facts

Serving Size 7 oz (211g)
Servings Per Container 8

Amount Per Serving

Calories 380   Calories from Fat 160

% Daily Value*

Total Fat 18g — 28%

Saturated Fat 4.5g — 23%

Trans Fat 0g

Cholesterol 115mg — 38%

Sodium 570mg — 24%

Total Carbohydrate 14g — 5%

Dietary Fiber 1g — 4%

Sugars 9g

Protein 39g

Vitamin A 2%   •   Vitamin C 20%

Calcium 4%   •   Iron 20%

*Percent Daily Values are based on a 2,000 calorie diet. Your daily values may be higher or lower depending on your calorie needs.

	Calories	2,000	2,500
Total Fat	Less than	65g	80g
Saturated Fat	Less than	20g	25g
Cholesterol	Less than	300mg	300mg
Sodium	Less than	2,400mg	2,400mg
Total Carbohydrate		300g	375g
Dietary Fiber		25g	30g

Calories per gram
Fat 9 • Carbohydrate 4 • Protein 4

Preheat your oven to 200° F.

Mix sea salt, black pepper, cumin and 1 1/2 tablespoons of oil in a small bowl; mix well. Season the roast on all sides. Heat a skillet over a high heat and sear the roast on all sides. Remove the roast, cover and set aside.

Reduce the heat to medium and add 2 tablespoons of oil; sauté the onion and garlic until the onion is translucent, about 5 minutes.

Pour in the tomato juice, balsamic vinegar, olive and raisin. Bring to a boil; boil until the liquid is reduced by half. Add the roast to a roasting pan and pour the tomato juice mixture over the roast.

Place in the oven to cook for about 3 to 3 1/2 hours until the meat is very tender; test with a fork. Internal temperature should read 160° F, at the thickest part. When cooked, remove from the oven; cover and let the meat rest for at least 30 minutes before serving.

Servings: 4

Target source of Protein, Dietary Fats, Vitamins B2, B3, B6, B12, Vitamin C, Iron, Phosphorus, Selenium, Zinc

Supportive of Immune Health

SUN-DRIED TOMATO STEAK SPIRALS

1/4 cup chopped fresh organic sun-dried tomato; no added oil

1/2 cup boiling water or organic beef broth; for flavor

1/4 cup chopped fresh parsley

1 tbsp prepared organic horseradish

1 1/5 tsp ground black pepper

2 tbsps extra virgin olive oil

2 1/4 lbs grass-fed flank steak or lean flank steak; Milanese

Twine or kitchen string

1/4 tsp fine grain sea salt

Nutrition Facts
Serving Size 7 oz (222g)
Servings Per Container 4

Amount Per Serving

Calories 480   Calories from Fat 270

% Daily Value*

Total Fat 30g — 46%

Saturated Fat 11g — 55%

Trans Fat 0g

Cholesterol 120mg — 40%

Sodium 170mg — 7%

Total Carbohydrate 3g — 1%

Dietary Fiber 1g — 4%

Sugars 0g

Protein 48g

Vitamin A 8% • Vitamin C 20%

Calcium 2% • Iron 35%

*Percent Daily Values are based on a 2,000 calorie diet. Your daily values may be higher or lower depending on your calorie needs.

	Calories	2,000	2,500
Total Fat	Less than	65g	80g
Saturated Fat	Less than	20g	25g
Cholesterol	Less than	300mg	300mg
Sodium	Less than	2,400mg	2,400mg
Total Carbohydrate		300g	375g
Dietary Fiber		25g	30g

Calories per gram
Fat 9 • Carbohydrate 4 • Protein 4

Preheat oven to 400° F.

Place sun-dried tomato in bowl and cover with water for 5 minutes to hydrate; drain. Add parsley, horseradish and black pepper and set aside.

Open meat so it lies flat; cover with plastic wrap and flatten to 1/4 inch thickness. Remove the plastic. Spoon the tomato mixture over meat to within 1/2-inch of edges. Roll up tightly in a roll, starting with the long side. Tie with kitchen string.

Line a sheet pan with aluminum foil and coat with cooking spray. Heat 2 tablespoons of oil in a large skillet over medium-high heat. Sear steak on both sides and place on lined baking dish.

Bake uncovered for 30-40 minutes. Internal temperature should read 160° F, at the thickest part. Let rest for 10 minutes. Remove the string and cut into slices. Season with sea salt and serve.

Servings: 4

Target source of Protein, Dietary Fats, Vitamins B1, B2, B3, B6, B12, Vitamin C, Vitamin K, Copper, Iron, Magnesium, Phosphorus, Potassium, Selenium, Zinc

Supportive of Immune Health

SURF N' TURF STEAK TOPPED WITH GRILLED SHRIMP

1 1/2 lbs grass-fed chuck eye beef steak, cut 1-inch thick

1/4 cup Montreal Seasoning, page 216

1 tsp fine grain sea salt

1 tsp ground black pepper

2 tbsps extra virgin olive oil, more as needed

16 large shrimp, shelled and de-veined

1 freshly squeezed lemon juice

Nutrition Facts

Serving Size 4 shrimp 5 oz steak (217g)

Servings Per Container 4

Amount Per Serving

Calories 470   Calories from Fat 240

	% Daily Value*
Total Fat 27g	42%
Saturated Fat 10g	50%
Trans Fat 1g	
Cholesterol 195mg	65%
Sodium 2080mg	87%
Total Carbohydrate 5g	2%
Dietary Fiber 1g	4%
Sugars 0g	
Protein 53g	

Vitamin A 6%	Vitamin C 6%
Calcium 8%	Iron 35%

*Percent Daily Values are based on a 2,000 calorie diet. Your daily values may be higher or lower depending on your calorie needs.

	Calories	2,000	2,500
Total Fat	Less than	65g	80g
Saturated Fat	Less than	20g	25g
Cholesterol	Less than	300mg	300mg
Sodium	Less than	2,400mg	2,400mg
Total Carbohydrate		300g	375g
Dietary Fiber		25g	30g

Calories per gram

Fat 9 • Carbohydrate 4 • Protein 4

Preheat oven to 375° F.

Prepare Montreal Seasoning.

Mix sea salt, ground pepper and montreal seasoning in a bowl. Season the steak on both sides. Place in the refrigerator for 15-30 minutes to marinade. Heat 2 tablespoons of oil in a skillet over medium-high heat and sear both sides.

Place on a sheet pan and cook in the oven for 10-15 minutes. Internal temperature should reach 140° F, at the thickest part. Remove sheet pan, cover and set aside. Heat 2 tablespoons of oil in a skillet over med-high heat. Add shrimp; sauté for 2-3 minutes. Turn and cook another 2 minutes or until just opaque. Do not overcook. Spoon shrimp over steak and season with sea salt and freshly squeezed lemon juice.

Serve shrimp on top of steak.

Servings: 4

Target source of Protein, Dietary Fats, Vitamins B1, B2, B3, B6, B12, Pantothenic Acid, Iron, Phosphorus, Potassium, Selenium, Zinc

Supportive of Immune Health

TEX-MEX GROUND BEEF SWEET POTATO BOATS

2 sweet potato boats, scooped

1/2 lb grass-fed ground beef or 93/7 lean ground beef

2 tbsps extra virgin olive oil

1/2 cup chopped onion

1 minced garlic clove

1 8 oz can organic stewed tomato

1 tsp ground organic chili powder

1/4 tbsp chopped fresh oregano or 1/4 tsp dried oregano

1/4 tsp ground cumin

1/4 tsp organic red pepper flake

1/4 tsp fine grain sea salt

1/8 tsp ground black pepper

Nutrition Facts

Serving Size 7 oz or 1 boat (207g)
Servings Per Container 4

Amount Per Serving	
Calories 210	Calories from Fat 80

	% Daily Value*
Total Fat 10g	15%
Saturated Fat 2g	10%
Trans Fat 0g	
Cholesterol 30mg	10%
Sodium 360mg	15%
Total Carbohydrate 19g	6%
Dietary Fiber 3g	12%
Sugars 6g	
Protein 13g	

Vitamin A 190%	•	Vitamin C 15%
Calcium 4%	•	Iron 10%

*Percent Daily Values are based on a 2,000 calorie diet. Your daily values may be higher or lower depending on your calorie needs

	Calories	2,000	2,500
Total Fat	Less than	65g	80g
Saturated Fat	Less than	20g	25g
Cholesterol	Less than	300mg	300mg
Sodium	Less than	2,400mg	2,400mg
Total Carbohydrate		300g	375g
Dietary Fiber		25g	30g

Calories per gram
Fat 9 • Carbohydrate 4 • Protein 4

Mix sea salt, ground pepper and Montreal seasoning in a bowl. Season the steak on both sides. Place in the refrigerator for 15-30 minutes to marinade. Heat 2 tablespoons of oil in a skillet over medium-high heat and sear both sides.

Place on a sheet pan and cook in the oven for 10-15 minutes. Internal temperature should reach 140° F, at the thickest part. Remove sheet pan, cover and set aside.

Heat 2 tablespoons of oil in a skillet over med-high heat. Add shrimp; sauté for 2-3 minutes. Turn and cook another 2 minutes or until just opaque. Do not overcook. Spoon shrimp over steak and season with sea salt and freshly squeezed lemon juice. Serve shrimp on top of steak.

Servings: 4

Target source of Protein, Dietary Fats, Vitamins B1, B2, B3, B6, B12, Pantothenic Acid, Iron, Phosphorus, Potassium, Selenium, Zinc

Supportive of Immune Health

ZESTY BEEF PICCADILLY

2 lbs grass-fed ground beef or 93/7 lean ground beef

2 minced garlic clove

3/4 cup chopped white onion

1 chopped organic green bell pepper

3 ribs chopped organic celery

1/2 cup dried golden raisin

1/2 cup Basic Tomato Sauce, page 250

2 tsps chipotle Tabasco sauce

1/2 tsp ground cumin

1/2 tsp fine grain sea salt

1/4 tsp ground black pepper

Nutrition Facts		
Serving Size 5 oz (152g)		
Servings Per Container 8		
Amount Per Serving		
Calories 250	Calories from Fat 140	
		% Daily Value*
Total Fat 16g		25%
Saturated Fat 7g		35%
Trans Fat 1g		
Cholesterol 55mg		18%
Sodium 320mg		13%
Total Carbohydrate 12g		4%
Dietary Fiber 1g		4%
Sugars 9g		
Protein 16g		
Vitamin A 4%	•	Vitamin C 15%
Calcium 2%	•	Iron 10%

*Percent Daily Values are based on a 2,000 calorie diet. Your daily values may be higher or lower depending on your calorie needs.

	Calories	2,000	2,500
Total Fat	Less than	65g	80g
Saturated Fat	Less than	20g	25g
Cholesterol	Less than	300mg	300mg
Sodium	Less than	2,400mg	2,400mg
Total Carbohydrate		300g	375g
Dietary Fiber		25g	30g

Calories per gram:
Fat 9 • Carbohydrate 4 • Protein 4

Prepare Tomato Sauce.

Heat a large skillet over medium-high heat; sauté ground beef and garlic until cooked through; no pink. Strain grease from beef and set beef aside; discard grease.

Add onion, bell pepper and celery to skillet; sauté for 10 minutes until vegetables are crisp tender and onions are translucent.

Add ground beef, raisin, tomato sauce, Tabasco, cumin, sea salt, and black pepper. Bring to boil; reduce heat, cover and simmer 10 minutes until most of liquid reduces; stirring occasionally. Add sauce to meat and serve.

Servings: 4

Target source of Protein, Dietary Fats, Vitamin C, Vitamin K, Iron

Supportive of Immune Health

CHICKEN

ANCHO-CHILI LIME GLAZED CHICKEN

4 free-range, pastured chicken breasts, cut into 1-inch
  cubes

1/2 tbsp organic chili powder

1/2 tbsp coconut oil

3/4 tsp coconut sugar

3/4 tsp minced garlic clove

3/4 tsp ground cumin

3/4 tsp fine grain sea salt

3/4 tsp ground black pepper

3 tbsps maple syrup, grade B

3/4 tbsp chipotle Tabasco Sauce

3/4 tbsp Clarified Butter, page 203

1 1/2 tbsps freshly squeezed lime juice

1/4 tsp crushed red pepper flake

1 tbsp chopped fresh cilantro or 1 tsps dried cilantro,
  garnish

Nutrition Facts

Serving Size 3 1/2 oz (101g)
Servings Per Container 8

Amount Per Serving

Calories 130	Calories from Fat 30

	% Daily Value*
Total Fat 3.5g	5%
Saturated Fat 1.5g	8%
Trans Fat 0g	
Cholesterol 50mg	17%
Sodium 310mg	13%
Total Carbohydrate 6g	2%
Dietary Fiber 0g	0%
Sugars 5g	
Protein 20g	

Vitamin A 2%	•	Vitamin C 2%
Calcium 0%	•	Iron 4%

*Percent Daily Values are based on a 2,000 calorie diet. Your daily values may be higher or lower depending on your calorie needs.

	Calories:	2,000	2,500
Total Fat	Less than	65g	80g
Saturated Fat	Less than	20g	25g
Cholesterol	Less than	300mg	300mg
Sodium	Less than	2,400mg	2,400mg
Total Carbohydrate		300g	375g
Dietary Fiber		25g	30g

Calories per gram:
Fat 9 • Carbohydrate 4 • Protein 4

Prepare Clarified Butter.

Wash and trim fat from chicken.In a medium bowl, combine chili powder, coconut oil, coconut sugar, garlic, cumin, sea salt and black pepper; mix well. Add chicken and toss to coat.

Heat clarified butter in a small saucepan over high heat. Add maple syrup, chipotle Tabasco sauce, clarified butter, lime juice and red peppers; bring to a boil. Turn down the heat slightly and simmer until mixture is reduced to 1/2 cup, about 3 minutes; sauce begins to thicken. Remove from heat and reserve; sauce will continue to thicken slightly.

Stove top grill pan: preheat grill over medium-high heat. Spray pan with cooking oil. Brush 2 tablespoons of reserved maple syrup mixture on each side of chicken. Add chicken to grill pan; cook 6 minutes on each side, or until cooked through.

Grill: Spray the grill with cooking oil. Brush 2 tablespoons of reserved syrup mixture on each side of chicken; grill for 8-15 minutes. Turn chicken over, brush again with 2 tablespoons of reserved syrup mixture: grill another 8-15 minutes or until done.

Garnish with cilantro. Brush any remaining maple syrup mixture and serve with a lime wedge.

Tip
Grill heat is indirect heat and will take longer to cook through.

Servings: 4

Target source of Protein and Iron

Supportive of Immune Health

APPLE CHICKEN

16 free-range, pastured chicken drumsticks and thighs, mixed

1/4 cup organic apple butter

1/4 cup maple syrup, grade B

1/2 tsp ground ginger

1/2 tsp fine grain sea salt

1/4 tsp ground black pepper

2 organic apples, cored, cut into 8 wedges

1/2 each freshly squeezed lemon juice; to prevent browning

Nutrition Facts

Serving Size 6 oz drumstick (275g)
Servings Per Container 4

Amount Per Serving

Calories 400   Calories from Fat 110

	% Daily Value*
Total Fat 12g	18%
Saturated Fat 3.5g	18%
Trans Fat 0g	
Cholesterol 200mg	67%
Sodium 930mg	39%
Total Carbohydrate 31g	10%
Dietary Fiber 2g	8%
Sugars 27g	
Protein 41g	

Vitamin A 0%	•	Vitamin C 8%	
Calcium 2%	•	Iron 10%	

*Percent Daily Values are based on a 2,000 calorie diet. Your daily values may be higher or lower depending on your calorie needs.

		Calories	2,000	2,500
Total Fat	Less than		65g	80g
Saturated Fat	Less than		20g	25g
Cholesterol	Less than		300mg	300mg
Sodium	Less than		2,400mg	2,400mg
Total Carbohydrate			300g	375g
Dietary Fiber			25g	30g

Calories per gram
Fat 9 • Carbohydrate 4 • Protein 4

Preheat oven to broil, 500° F.

In a zip lock bag, add apple butter, maple syrup, ground ginger, sea salt and black pepper; mix well. Add the drumsticks and toss to coat. Place in the refrigerator for 15-30 minutes to marinade.

Line a sheet pan with aluminum foil and transfer drumsticks to pan; reserve glaze. Add apple wedges and broil for 13 to 15 minutes. Turn drumsticks occasionally and brush on reserved glaze. Internal temperature of chicken should read 165° F, at the thickest part. Serve apple slices on the side.

Servings: 8

Target source of Protein, Iron, Vitamin C, Dietary Fats, Magnesium

Supportive of Immune Health

APRICOT GLAZED CHICKEN

4 free-range thighs; rinse and trim fat

4 free-range drumsticks; rinse and trim fat

5 tbsps extra virgin olive oil, divided

1 1/2 cups chopped onion

2 chopped organic Fuji apple, cored

1 each chopped organic celery stalk

2 minced garlic clove

1/4 cup chopped organic dried golden raisin

1 1/2 cups chopped organic dried apricot

1/4 cup chopped walnut

1 free-range egg, beaten

1/4 tsp fine grain sea salt

1/4 tsp ground black pepper

1 tbsp Poultry Seasoning, page 217

3/4 cup organic apricot preserve

1 cup freshly squeezed orange juice

Nutrition Facts

Serving Size 2 (188g)

Servings Per Container 8

Amount Per Serving

Calories 320 — Calories from Fat 130

% Daily Value*

Total Fat 15g	23%
Saturated Fat 3.5g	18%
Trans Fat 0g	
Cholesterol 85mg	28%
Sodium 80mg	3%
Total Carbohydrate 27g	9%
Dietary Fiber 2g	8%
Sugars 19g	
Protein 21g	

Vitamin A 4% • Vitamin C 25%

Calcium 4% • Iron 10%

*Percent Daily Values are based on a 2,000 calorie diet. Your daily values may be higher or lower depending on your calorie needs.

	Calories	2,000	2,500
Total Fat	Less than	65g	80g
Saturated Fat	Less than	20g	25g
Cholesterol	Less than	300mg	300mg
Sodium	Less than	2,400mg	2,400mg
Total Carbohydrate		300g	375g
Dietary Fiber		25g	30g

Calories per gram:

Fat 9 • Carbohydrate 4 • Protein 4

Preheat oven to 400° F.

Prepare Poultry Seasoning.

Heat 2 tablespoons of oil over in a skillet over medium-high heat. Add onion, apple, celery and garlic; sauté until tender, about 3 minutes. Add golden raisin, dried apricot, walnut and egg to mixture and mix well; sauté for 3 minutes to incorporate egg. Add sea salt and black pepper, to taste.

Arrange the chicken in a baking dish lined with foil. Seasoning: mix together the remaining 3 tablespoons of oil and poultry seasoning. Brush over chicken. Glaze: Mash apricot preserve and orange juice. Brush over chicken.

Bake uncovered for 30 minutes. Reduce the oven heat to 325° F. Continue roasting and basting with apricot glaze every 20 minutes, until cooked through and meat is very tender. The internal temperature should reach 165° F, at the thickest part. Remove the chicken from the oven and let rest for 7-10 minutes to fully cook.

Servings: 4

Target source of Protein, Selenium, Dietary Fiber

Support of Immune and Gut Health

ORANGE-CRANBERRY CHICKEN WITH TOASTED WALNUTS

4 free-range, pastured chicken breast, whole

1 tbsp Poultry Seasoning, page 217

1/4 tsp fine grain sea salt

1/4 tsp ground black pepper

2 tbsps extra virgin olive oil

1 large freshly squeezed orange juice

1/3 cup orange preserve

1/2 cup dried cranberry

Dash white wine vinegar

1/3 cup coconut milk, full fat; in a can

1/4 cup chopped Toasted Walnut, page 241

1/4 cup organic chicken broth

1 organic orange zest, garnish

Nutrition Facts

Serving Size 6 oz (290g)
Servings Per Container 4

Amount Per Serving

Calories 400   Calories from Fat 160

	% Daily Value*
Total Fat 18g	28%
Saturated Fat 5g	25%
Trans Fat 0g	
Cholesterol 100mg	33%
Sodium 310mg	13%
Total Carbohydrate 24g	8%
Dietary Fiber 1g	4%
Sugars 14g	
Protein 41g	

Vitamin A 4%	•	Vitamin C 40%	
Calcium 2%	•	Iron 10%	

*Percent Daily Values are based on a 2,000 calorie diet. Your daily values may be higher or lower depending on your calorie needs.

	Calories	2,000	2,500
Total Fat	Less than	65g	80g
Saturated Fat	Less than	20g	25g
Cholesterol	Less than	300mg	300mg
Sodium	Less than	2,400mg	2,400mg
Total Carbohydrate		300g	375g
Dietary Fiber		25g	30g

Calories per gram:
Fat 9 • Carbohydrate 4 • Protein 4

Preheat oven to 400° F.

Prepare Poultry Seasoning and Toasted Walnut.

Trim the fat and wash your chicken. Sprinkle poultry seasoning, sea salt and black pepper over chicken.

Heat the oil in a skillet over medium-high heat. Once hot, add the chicken; cook about 4-5 minutes until golden brown. Flip and cook another 4-5 minutes until golden brown. Remove the seared chicken and place on a sheet pan sprayed with cooking oil. Bake for 20 minutes.

Add coconut milk; stir frequently. Add the chicken back to the skillet. Cover and simmer over medium-low heat for about 5 minutes; stir occasionally. Deglaze skillet with chicken broth; scrape the bottom of pan with a wooden spoon. Add orange juice, preserve, vinegar, and cranberry. Boil for approximately 3-4 minutes.

Remove the sauce from the heat and add toasted walnuts. Garnish with orange zest.

Tips
Vinegar wash: 4 to 1 ratio, water to vinegar mix will wash chicken; even if you buy free-range, it's great to get the residue off.

Coconut Oil full fat, in a can, should only contain two to three natural ingredients. I get mine from an Asian Market.

Servings: 4

Target source of Protein, Dietary Fats, Vitamin C, Iron, Copper, Manganese

Supportive of Immune Health

ROSEMARY HERB CHICKEN BITES

4 free-range, pastured boneless and skinless chicken
   breast, cut into 1-inch cubes

2 tbsps extra virgin olive oil, more if needed

1/2 tsp fine grain sea salt, to taste

1/2 tsp ground black pepper, to taste

1 1/2 tbsps minced fresh rosemary or 1 1/2 tsp dried
   rosemary

Nutrition Facts

Serving Size 6 oz (179g)
Servings Per Container 4

Amount Per Serving

Calories 240   Calories from Fat 80

	% Daily Value*
Total Fat 9g	14%
Saturated Fat 1g	5%
Trans Fat 0g	
Cholesterol 95mg	32%
Sodium 400mg	17%
Total Carbohydrate 0g	0%
Dietary Fiber 0g	0%
Sugars 0g	
Protein 39g	

Vitamin A 0%	•	Vitamin C 0%
Calcium 0%	•	Iron 6%

*Percent Daily Values are based on a 2,000 calorie diet. Your daily values may be higher or lower depending on your calorie needs.

		Calories:	2,000	2,500
Total Fat	Less than		65g	80g
Saturated Fat	Less than		20g	25g
Cholesterol	Less than		300mg	300mg
Sodium	Less than		2,400mg	2,400mg
Total Carbohydrate			300g	375g
Dietary Fiber			25g	30g

Calories per gram
Fat 9 • Carbohydrate 4 • Protein 4

Place chicken, oil, sea salt, black pepper and rosemary into resealable plastic bag; knead bag to coat chicken.

Heat the oil in a large skillet over medium-high heat. Add chicken, sear for 3 minutes on both sides. Then cook an additional 3-5 minutes on each side. Internal temperature should read 165° F, at the thickest part; no pink. Add a little oil as needed to skillet.

Servings: 4

Target Source of Protein and Iron

Supportive of Immune Health

SEARED CHICKEN IN A LUSCIOUS POMEGRANATE SAUCE

1/4 cup organic pomegranate juice

2 cups coarsely chopped walnut

4 tbsps extra virgin olive oil

4 free-range, pastured chicken breast, 6 oz each

1 large finely chopped red onion

2 crushed garlic clove

2 tbsps organic tomato paste

1 cup organic chicken broth

1/2 tsp turmeric

1 tsp ground cinnamon

1 tbsp coconut sugar

1/2 tsp fine grain sea salt, to taste

1/2 tsp ground black pepper, to taste

Nutrition Facts

Serving Size 6 oz piece (434g)
Servings Per Container 4

Amount Per Serving

Calories 770   Calories from Fat 490

	% Daily Value*
Total Fat 55g	**85%**
Saturated Fat 6g	**30%**
Trans Fat 0g	
Cholesterol 100mg	**33%**
Sodium 630mg	**26%**
Total Carbohydrate 29g	**10%**
Dietary Fiber 6g	**24%**
Sugars 17g	
Protein 49g	

Vitamin A 2%	•	Vitamin C 10%	
Calcium 8%	•	Iron 20%	

*Percent Daily Values are based on a 2,000 calorie diet. Your daily values may be higher or lower depending on your calorie needs.

		Calories	2,000	2,500
Total Fat	Less than		65g	80g
Saturated Fat	Less than		20g	25g
Cholesterol	Less than		300mg	300mg
Sodium	Less than		2,400mg	2,400mg
Total Carbohydrate			300g	375g
Dietary Fiber			25g	30g

Calories per gram
Fat 9 • Carbohydrate 4 • Protein 4

Grind walnuts to a paste in a food processor. Mix in pomegranate juice and process to a thick liquid.

Heat the oil in a large skillet in a large skillet. Add chicken; sauté until browned on both sides. Do not cook all the way through. Remove and set aside on covered plate.

In the same skillet over medium-high heat, add onion and garlic; sauté over medium heat until onion is soft. Reduce heat to low and stir in tomato paste; sauté for 1-1/2 minutes; stirring constantly to break down paste. Slowly add the walnut mixture; stir to incorporate. Add chicken broth, turmeric, cinnamon, and coconut sugar: cover and simmer for 35 minutes; chicken should be tender and cooked through. Internal temperature should read 165° F.

Servings: 4

Target source of Protein, Dietary Fats, Vitamins B1, B6, Folate, Copper, Iron, Magnesium, Manganese, Molybdenum, Phosphorus, Potassium, Zinc

Supportive of Immune Health

SPINACH STUFFED CHICKEN ROLLS

3/4 cup chopped onion

3/4 cup chopped organic celery

3/4 cup chopped organic red bell pepper

2 minced garlic clove

1 tbsp Clarified Butter, page 203

2 cups fresh organic spinach leaf, with stem

1 free-range egg, beaten

2 cups Almond Bread Crumb, page 166

6 free-range, pastured chicken breasts, 6 oz each

2 tbsps almond meal

1 cup organic chicken stock

1 tsp freshly squeezed lemon juice

2 cups sliced mushroom

1/4 tsp Lemon Pepper Seasoning, page 215

Nutrition Facts

Serving Size 6 oz piece (13 oz total weight) (394g)
Servings Per Container 6

Amount Per Serving

Calories 510   Calories from Fat 240

	% Daily Value*
Total Fat 27g	42%
Saturated Fat 4g	20%
Trans Fat 0g	
Cholesterol 290mg	97%
Sodium 570mg	24%
Total Carbohydrate 17g	6%
Dietary Fiber 6g	24%
Sugars 7g	
Protein 52g	

Vitamin A 45%	•	Vitamin C 50%	
Calcium 10%	•	Iron 20%	

*Percent Daily Values are based on a 2,000 calorie diet. Your daily values may be higher or lower depending on your calorie needs.

		Calories	2,000	2,500
Total Fat	Less than		65g	80g
Saturated Fat	Less than		20g	25g
Cholesterol	Less than		300mg	300mg
Sodium	Less than		2,400mg	2,400mg
Total Carbohydrate			300g	375g
Dietary Fiber			25g	30g

Calories per gram:
Fat 9 • Carbohydrate 4 • Protein 4

Preheat the oven to 350° F.

Prepare Clarified Butter, Almond Bread, Lemon Pepper Seasoning and Mushroom Sauce.

Heat 1 tablespoon of clarified butter in a skillet on medium-high heat. Add onion, celery, bell pepper and garlic; sauté until onions are translucent, stirring often. Add spinach; stir until wilted. Reduce heat to medium, and let cool slightly, for 2 minutes. Add egg and almond bread crumbs; stirring until combined.

Flatten chicken to 1/4-inch thick; cover chicken with plastic wrap and pound with a mallet. Place chicken in a baking dish sprayed with cooking oil. Spoon the spinach mixture over each piece of chicken. Roll up chicken and place toothpicks to close. Alternatively, twine or kitchen string will work.

Sprinkle with lemon pepper, cover and bake for 40-45 minutes until chicken juices run clear. Internal temperature of chicken should read 165° F, at the thickest area.

Remove toothpicks from roll-ups and top with mushroom sauce.

Servings: 6

Target source of Protein, Dietary Fats, Vitamin A, Vitamin C, B12, Folate, Vitamin K, Iron, Magnesium

Supportive of Immune and Detoxification Health

TURKEY

CARIBBEAN TURKEY STEW

2 1/2 lbs skinless free-range, pastured turkey thighs

1 tbsp extra virgin olive oil

1 1/2 cups thinly sliced onion

1/2 tsp red pepper flake

1/2 tsp fine grain sea salt

1/4 cup unsweetened coconut flake

1 cup organic chicken broth

1/4 cup diced dried pineapple

1/2 cup organic stewed tomato

1 lb butternut squash, peeled and cut into 1-inch cubes

1 lb sweet potato, peeled and cut into 1-inch cubes

GARNISH
2 sliced bananas
5 sliced green onion
1/2 cup unsweetenesd coconut flakes
2 lime wedges

Nutrition Facts

Serving Size 5 oz piece (13 oz total weight) (369g)
Servings Per Container 8

Amount Per Serving

Calories 370	Calories from Fat 120

	% Daily Value*
Total Fat 13g	20%
Saturated Fat 7g	35%
Trans Fat 0g	
Cholesterol 115mg	38%
Sodium 540mg	23%
Total Carbohydrate 34g	11%
Dietary Fiber 6g	24%
Sugars 15g	
Protein 30g	

Vitamin A 350%	•	Vitamin C 45%	
Calcium 8%	•	Iron 15%	

*Percent Daily Values are based on a 2,000 calorie diet. Your daily values may be higher or lower depending on your calorie needs:

	Calories	2,000	2,500
Total Fat	Less than	65g	80g
Saturated Fat	Less than	20g	25g
Cholesterol	Less than	300mg	300mg
Sodium	Less than	2,400mg	2,400mg
Total Carbohydrate		300g	375g
Dietary Fiber		25g	30g

Calories per gram
Fat 9 • Carbohydrate 4 • Protein 4

In a stockpot or Dutch oven, heat the oil over medium-high heat. Sear the thighs on both sides, about 3 minutes per side. Remove and set aside.

Scrape the bottom of the pan with a wooden spoon. Add onions; sauté for 2 to 3 minutes until translucent. Add red pepper flake, sea salt, coconut flake, broth, pineapple, tomato, squash, sweet potato and turkey thigh. Bring to a boil; reduce heat to medium, cover and simmer 1 1/2 hours. Internal temperature should read 165° F, at the thickest part.

Remove thighs from the stew and strip the meat from the bones with a fork. Return the meat to the stew and simmer for 5 minutes to heat through.

To serve, spoon stew into bowls and garnish with banana, green onion and coconut flake. Squeeze fresh lime juice over top.

Servings: 6

Target source of Protein, Dietary Fats, Dietary Fiber, B Vitamins, Vitamin A, Vitamin C, Pantothenic Acid, Calcium, Copper, Iron, Magnesium, Manganese, Phosphorus, Potassium, Selenium, Zinc

Supportive of Immune and Gut Health

88.

AFFIRMATIONS

Chef Patricia catered an event of mine in 2012 at the UMLAF Sculpture Garden in Austin, Texas. From the moment I met her I fell in love. Her level of professionalism, dedication and love of food us unparalleled. **Chef Cashion had the tough task of making a generally un-paleo friendly audience fall in love with her food- and she succeeded. Her quail lollipops were a hit and she even made paleo-friendly, low sugar cake pops that people were raving about all night!** *To top it all off, she has a magnificent eye for staging, and designed not only the food, but the table set up in such an elegant and tasteful way that fit the theme of our event. I know my event could have not been as memorable without her.* **Our guest left feeling full, but happy and energetic!**

--Lauren F., Las Angeles, California
LafCreative

I've had the honor to have tasted some of the incredible dishes constructed by this exceptional culinary chef. I know the author to be extensively well researched, dedicated to culinary and optimal health integrity, and to be an extraordinary master of the kitchen. Patricia has never disappointed. Indeed, her recipes are the path to delectable delights and high health.

--Judith Ruder, Austin, Texas
Paleo Café by Public Awareness Media

KALE TURKEY BURGERS WITH SUN-DRIED TOMATO

2 lbs free-range, pastured ground turkey

1 cup dried organic sun-dried tomato

1 1/2 cups organic chicken broth

3 cups finely chopped organic kale

1 large free-range egg

1-2 tbsps chipotle Tabasco sauce; flavorful, not spicy

3 tbsps Dijon Mustard, page 228

1 tbsp garlic powder

2 tsp onion powder

1 tsp dried thyme

1/2 tbsp fresh chopped rosemary or 1/2 tsp dried rosemary

1 tsp fine grain sea salt

1/2 tsp ground black pepper

Nutrition Facts

Serving Size 5 oz (155g)
Servings Per Container 8

Amount Per Serving

Calories 220   Calories from Fat 70

% Daily Value*

Total Fat 8g	**12%**
Saturated Fat 1g	**5%**
Trans Fat 0g	
Cholesterol 85mg	**28%**
Sodium 560mg	**23%**
Total Carbohydrate 12g	**4%**
Dietary Fiber 2g	**8%**
Sugars 5g	
Protein 27g	

Vitamin A 15%	•	Vitamin C 20%
Calcium 2%	•	Iron 10%

*Percent Daily Values are based on a 2,000 calorie diet. Your daily values may be higher or lower depending on your calorie needs.

	Calories	2,000	2,500
Total Fat	Less than	65g	80g
Saturated Fat	Less than	20g	25g
Cholesterol	Less than	300mg	300mg
Sodium	Less than	2,400mg	2,400mg
Total Carbohydrate		300g	375g
Dietary Fiber		25g	30g

Calories per gram:
Fat 9 • Carbohydrate 4 • Protein 4

Preheat the grill on medium-high heat.

Prepare the Dijon Mustard and soak Sun-Dried Tomatoes.

Heat the chicken broth in a saucepan over high heat; bring to a boil, remove from heat and add sun-dried tomatoes. Soak for 15 minutes.

Combine ALL ingredients into a large bowl; mix well. Gather about 2 ounces and make 12-16 burgers.

Spray grill with cooking spray. Grill burgers for 4-5 minutes on one side. Flip with a metal spatula; grill for another 8-10 minutes until juices run clear. Internal temperature should read 160° F, at the thickest part.

Tips
Freeze for later.

Alternatively, you can use a large skillet or grill pan.

Target source of High in Protein! The kale adds only 100 calories to the overall recipe.

Servings: 8

Target source of Protein, Vitamin A, Vitamin C, Vitamin K, Iron

Supportive of Immune Health

ROASTED TURKEY LEGS WITH CRANBERRY-JEZEBEL SAUCE

SAUCE

1 3/4 cups organic chicken broth

1/2 cup coconut sugar

1 1/4 cups dried cranberry

1/2 cup organic pineapple preserve

1 tsp organic prepared horseradish

1 tbsp Dijon Mustard, page 228

TURKEY LEGS

6 free-pastured turkey legs

1 tsp fine grain sea salt, to taste

1 tsp ground black pepper, to taste

3 tbsps extra virgin coconut oil

1 1/2 tsp Poultry Seasoning, page 217

Nutrition Facts

Serving Size 3 oz turkey leg (235g)
Servings Per Container 6

Amount Per Serving

Calories 470   Calories from Fat 160

	% Daily Value*
Total Fat 18g	28%
Saturated Fat 9g	45%
Trans Fat 0g	
Cholesterol 75mg	25%
Sodium 450mg	19%
Total Carbohydrate 54g	18%
Dietary Fiber 1g	4%
Sugars 51g	
Protein 24g	

Vitamin A 2%	•	Vitamin C 25%
Calcium 4%	•	Iron 10%

*Percent Daily Values are based on a 2,000 calorie diet. Your daily values may be higher or lower depending on your calorie needs

	Calories	2,000	2,500
Total Fat	Less than	65g	80g
Saturated Fat	Less than	20g	25g
Cholesterol	Less than	300mg	300mg
Sodium	Less than	2,400mg	2,400mg
Total Carbohydrate		300g	375g
Dietary Fiber		25g	30g

Calories per gram:
Fat 9 • Carbohydrate 4 • Protein 4

SAUCE

Heat broth and coconut sugar over medium-high heat to boiling; add cranberries, return to a boil. Reduce heat and simmer for 10 minutes until cranberries hydrate. Remove the saucepan from the heat and strain cranberries; reserve infused cranberry liquid.

In a small skillet over medium heat, add the cranberry, preserve and horseradish, sauté for 3 minutes until combined and sauce thickens; stirring occasionally.

TURKEY LEGS

Sprinkle turkey legs with sea salt and black pepper. Combine oil and poultry seasoning; mix well. Baste the turkey legs and roast in the oven 50 minutes until cooked through. Baste occasionally with any remaining seasoning.

Make more, if needed. Internal temperature should read 165° F, at the thickest part. Ladle the sauce over turkey and serve.

Tips

Sauce can be prepared ahead of time. Store in airtight container in refrigerator, for up to 2 weeks.

If you do not have time to prepare fresh, you can use organic Dijon mustard in substitutions. Be sure the ingredients are simple.

Servings: 4

Target source of Protein, Dietary Fats, Vitamins B2, B3, B6, Vitamin C, Iron, Phosphorus, Selenium, Zinc

Supportive of Immune Health

SLOPPY TURKEY

2 tbsps extra virgin olive oil

1 cup chopped onion

1 cup chopped organic green bell pepper, seeds and ribs
  removed

2 minced garlic clove

1 1/2 lbs ground pastured turkey

1 cup Chili Sauce, page 257

2 tbsps coconut aminos

1/2 tsp fine grain sea salt

1/2 tsp ground black pepper

Nutrition Facts

Serving Size 6 oz (166g)
Servings Per Container 8

Amount Per Serving	
Calories 210	Calories from Fat 90

	% Daily Value*
Total Fat 10g	15%
Saturated Fat 1.5g	8%
Trans Fat 0g	
Cholesterol 45mg	15%
Sodium 460mg	19%
Total Carbohydrate 12g	4%
Dietary Fiber 1g	4%
Sugars 7g	
Protein 19g	

Vitamin A 6%	•	Vitamin C 25%	
Calcium 2%	•	Iron 8%	

*Percent Daily Values are based on a 2,000 calorie diet. Your daily values may be higher or lower depending on your calorie needs.

		Calories	2,000	2,500
Total Fat	Less than		65g	80g
Saturated Fat	Less than		20g	25g
Cholesterol	Less than		300mg	300mg
Sodium	Less than		2,400mg	2,400mg
Total Carbohydrate			300g	375g
Dietary Fiber			25g	30g

Calories per gram
Fat 9 • Carbohydrate 4 • Protein 4

Prepare Chili Sauce.

Heat the oil in a large skillet over medium-high heat. Add onion and bell pepper; sauté until onions are translucent, about 5 minutes. Add garlic; sauté for 1 minute.

Add turkey; sauté about 5 minutes, stirring occasionally until no pink. Stir in chili sauce, coconut aminos, sea salt and black pepper; mix well.

Reduce heat to low, cover and simmer for 10 minutes.

Servings: 8

Target source of Protein, Vitamin C, Vitamin A, Iron

Supportive of Immune Health

TURKEY WALNUT ROMAINE TACOS

1 lb grass-fed ground beef or 93/7 lean ground beef, 3-4 oz each

1 tbsp coconut oil

1 chopped organic red bell pepper

1/2 cup chopped white onion

2 tbsps coconut oil, divided

1 1/2 tbsps chopped fresh oregano or 1 1/2 tsps dried oregano

2 tbsps chopped cilantro

1 1/2 tsps ground cumin

1 1/2 tsps chili powder

1/2 tsp fine grain sea salt, to taste

1 1/2 tbsps extra virgin olive oil

1 cup Toasted Walnut, page 241

4 organic romaine lettuce leafs

Nutrition Facts		
Serving Size 4 wraps (208g)		
Servings Per Container 4		
Amount Per Serving		
Calories 350	Calories from Fat 250	
		% Daily Value*
Total Fat 28g		43%
Saturated Fat 4g		20%
Trans Fat 0g		
Cholesterol 45mg		15%
Sodium 380mg		16%
Total Carbohydrate 7g		2%
Dietary Fiber 4g		16%
Sugars 2g		
Protein 22g		
Vitamin A 140%	•	Vitamin C 6%
Calcium 6%	•	Iron 20%

*Percent Daily Values are based on a 2,000 calorie diet. Your daily values may be higher or lower depending on your calorie needs.

	Calories	2,000	2,500
Total Fat	Less than	65g	80g
Saturated Fat	Less than	20g	25g
Cholesterol	Less than	300mg	300mg
Sodium	Less than	2,400mg	2,400mg
Total Carbohydrate		300g	375g
Dietary Fiber		25g	30g

Calories per gram:
Fat 9 • Carbohydrate 4 • Protein 4

TOPPING OPTIONS

1 1/2 cups sliced organic bell peppers; choose a variety of colors

1/2 cup chopped white onion

1/2 chopped green onion

1 tsp freshly squeezed lime juice

Cashew Sour Cream, page 224

Sliced avocado and cilantro

Original Tabasco hot sauce

Prepare Toasted Walnuts.

Wash romaine and place in a strainer to drain water.

Heat 1 tablespoon of oil in a skillet over medium heat. Add the pepper and onion; sauté for 7-10 minutes until soft. Reduce heat as needed; stirring frequently. Add 1 tablespoon of oil to the skillet. Add the oregano, cumin, chili powder, sea salt and water; mix well.

Add the beef; sauté for about 5 minutes, stirring occasionally. Strain grease and set aside. BUILD your Romaine Taco.

Servings: 4

Target source of Folate, Vitamin B3, B12, Copper, Zinc, Manganese, Vitamin K, Vitamin A, Protein, Dietary Fiber, Dietary Fats

Supportive of Immune, Detoxification and Neurological Health

PORK

BBQ PORK SPARE RIBS

3 lbs lean pastured pork spareribs, bone-in or boneless
1/2 tsp fine grain sea salt
1/2 tsp ground black pepper
1 tsp ground paprika
1/2 tsp ground dry mustard
1 minced garlic clove
3 tbsps Mother's apple cider vinegar
3/4 cup Basic Tomato Sauce, page 250
1/3 cup chopped onion
1 1/2 tsps organic chili powder
1/2 tsp fine grain sea salt
1/4 tsp ground black pepper
1/2 tbsp chopped fresh oregano or 1/2 tbsp dried oregano
1/2 cup water

Nutrition Facts

Serving Size 6 1/2 oz (186g)
Servings Per Container 8

Amount Per Serving

Calories 470	Calories from Fat 310

	% Daily Value*
Total Fat 34g	52%
Saturated Fat 12g	60%
Trans Fat 0g	
Cholesterol 130mg	43%
Sodium 520mg	22%
Total Carbohydrate 7g	2%
Dietary Fiber 1g	4%
Sugars 3g	
Protein 32g	

Vitamin A 8%	•	Vitamin C 2%
Calcium 6%	•	Iron 15%

*Percent Daily Values are based on a 2,000 calorie diet. Your daily values may be higher or lower depending on your calorie needs.

	Calories	2,000	2,500
Total Fat	Less than	65g	80g
Saturated Fat	Less than	20g	25g
Cholesterol	Less than	300mg	300mg
Sodium	Less than	2,400mg	2,400mg
Total Carbohydrate		300g	375g
Dietary Fiber		25g	30g

Calories per gram:
Fat 9 • Carbohydrate 4 • Protein 4

Preheat oven to 350° F.

Trim excess fat from ribs. Mix sea salt, black pepper, paprika and dry mustard; mix. Rub mixture onto ribs. Cut into 4 serving portions and place on a baking sheet pan sprayed with cooking oil. Bake for 45 to 60 minutes. Remove pan from oven and discard fat.

In a medium mixing bowl, combine minced garlic, vinegar, tomato sauce, onion, chili powder, sea salt and black pepper; mix well. Pour over the ribs. Cover with aluminum foil and let stand 15 minutes. Return ribs to oven, covered, and bake for 90 minutes. Remove the foil, baste with mixture, and bake for an additional 1/2 hour. Remove the excess fat before serving. Sprinkle with fresh oregano and serve.

Servings: 8

Target source of Protein, Dietary Fats, B Vitamins, Iron, Selenium, Phosphorus, Zinc, Vitamin D

Supportive of Immune and Detoxification Health

BRAISED PORK CUTLETS

4 tenderized pastured pork sirloin cutlets, about 1/4-inch
    thick, 6 oz each

4 tbsps almond flour

1/2 tsp fine grain sea salt

1 tsp ground black pepper

2 tsps Clarified Butter, page 203

1/2 cup organic vegetable stock

1/2 cup brewed green tea

2 tbsps Mother's apple cider vinegar

2 tbsps Dijon Mustard, page 228

2 tsps coconut sugar

2 tsps ground dill weed

Nutrition Facts

Serving Size 6 oz (169g)
Servings Per Container 4

Amount Per Serving

Calories 220	Calories from Fat 90

	% Daily Value*
Total Fat 10g	15%
Saturated Fat 3.5g	18%
Trans Fat 0g	
Cholesterol 70mg	23%
Sodium 490mg	20%
Total Carbohydrate 6g	2%
Dietary Fiber 1g	4%
Sugars 3g	
Protein 25g	

Vitamin A 4%	•	Vitamin C 2%
Calcium 4%	•	Iron 6%

*Percent Daily Values are based on a 2,000 calorie diet. Your daily values may be higher or lower depending on your calorie needs.

	Calories	2,000	2,500
Total Fat	Less than	65g	80g
Saturated Fat	Less than	20g	25g
Cholesterol	Less than	300mg	300mg
Sodium	Less than	2,400mg	2,400mg
Total Carbohydrate		300g	375g
Dietary Fiber		25g	30g

Calories per gram:
Fat 9 • Carbohydrate 4 • Protein 4

Prepare Clarified Butter and Dijon Mustard.

Brew green tea. Boil 1 cup of water and add green tea bag. Let tea bag simmer for 10-15 minutes.

Slightly tenderize the pork using a mallet to lightly pound meat. In a medium mixing bowl, combine almond flour, sea salt and black pepper; mix well. Dredge cutlets.

Melt clarified butter in a skillet over medium-high heat. Sear cutlets for 1-2 minutes, on both sides. Add vegetable stock, vinegar, Dijon mustard, coconut sugar and dill weed. Bring to a boil; reduce heat and simmer for 10-12 minutes until pork is cooked through. Internal Temperature should read 160° F, at thickest part. Remove cutlets and cover to keep warm. Boil the pan juices until thickened, stirring often. Pour pan juices over cutlets and serve.

Servings: 4

Target source of Phosphorus, Selenium, Vitamins B1, B3, B6, Protein

Supportive of Immune Health

GRILLED ONION PORK CHOPS

4 thinly sliced pastured pork chops

1/2 tsp fine grain sea salt

1/2 tsp ground black pepper

3 tbsps extra virgin olive oil, divided

1 1/2 cups sliced onion

Nutrition Facts
Serving Size 1 pork chop (197g)
Servings Per Container 4

Amount Per Serving

Calories 310   Calories from Fat 160

% Daily Value*

Total Fat 18g   28%

Saturated Fat 4g   20%

Trans Fat 0g

Cholesterol 90mg   30%

Sodium 390mg   16%

Total Carbohydrate 4g   1%

Dietary Fiber 1g   4%

Sugars 2g

Protein 32g

Vitamin A 0%   •   Vitamin C 6%

Calcium 2%   •   Iron 0%

*Percent Daily Values are based on a 2,000 calorie diet. Your daily values may be higher or lower depending on your calorie needs.

	Calories	2,000	2,500
Total Fat	Less than	65g	80g
Saturated Fat	Less than	20g	25g
Cholesterol	Less than	300mg	300mg
Sodium	Less than	2,400mg	2,400mg
Total Carbohydrate		300g	375g
Dietary Fiber		25g	30g

Calories per gram:
Fat 9   •   Carbohydrate 4   •   Protein 4

Season pork chops on both sides with sea salt and black pepper. Heat 2 tablespoons in a large skillet over medium-high heat. Add pork chops; sauté for about 3-5 minutes. Internal temperature should read 160° F, at the thickest part. Remove from the skillet, cover and set aside.

Heat 1 tablespoon of oil in a skillet over medium-high heat. Add onions; sauté for 5 minutes until onions begin to b rown. Serve caramelized onion over pork chop.

Servings: 4

Target source of Protein and Dietary Fats

Supportive of Immune Health

PORK CHOPS WITH BLUEBERRY HERB SAUCE

4 boneless pastured pork chops, about 3/4-inch thick

1 minced garlic clove

1/2 tsp fine grain sea salt

1 tsp ground black pepper

2 tbsps extra virgin olive oil

2 cups fresh blueberry

1/4 cup local raw honey

2 tbsps chopped fresh basil or 2 tspsdried basil

1 tbsp Mother's apple cider vinegar

1/4 tbsp fresh chopped thyme or 1/4 tsp dried thyme

1/4 tbsp fresh chopped sage or 1/4 tsp dried sage

Nutrition Facts		
Serving Size 1 pork chop (254g)		
Servings Per Container 4		
Amount Per Serving		
Calories 390	Calories from Fat 150	
		% Daily Value*
Total Fat 17g		26%
Saturated Fat 4g		20%
Trans Fat 0g		
Cholesterol 90mg		30%
Sodium 390mg		16%
Total Carbohydrate 29g		10%
Dietary Fiber 2g		8%
Sugars 23g		
Protein 32g		
Vitamin A 2%	•	Vitamin C 15%
Calcium 2%	•	Iron 2%

*Percent Daily Values are based on a 2,000 calorie diet. Your daily values may be higher or lower depending on your calorie needs.

		Calories	2,000	2,500
Total Fat	Less than		65g	80g
Saturated Fat	Less than		20g	25g
Cholesterol	Less than		300mg	300mg
Sodium	Less than		2,400mg	2,400mg
Total Carbohydrate			300g	375g
Dietary Fiber			25g	30g

Calories per gram
Fat 9 • Carbohydrate 4 • Protein 4

Combine garlic, sea salt, and black pepper. Rub on both sides of the pork. Cover pork chop with plastic wrap and pound with a mallet to 1/2 inch thick.

Heat 2 tablespoons of oil in a skillet over medium-high heat and sear pork chops, about 2 minutes each side. Cook an additional 3 minutes on each side; no pink. Internal temperature should read 160° F. Remove pork chops from the skillet, cover and set aside.

In same skillet over medium heat, add 2 teaspoons of oil, blueberry, honey, basil, vinegar, thyme and sage; sauté until thickened. Serve over pork.

Servings: 4

Target source of Protein, Dietary Fats, Vitamin C, Vitamin K, Manganese, B Vitamins, Antioxidants

Supportive of Immune Health

PORK MEATBALLS WITH ALMOND BREAD CRUMBS

2 1/2 lbs uncured, pastured ground pork

2 tbsps dried minced onion

1 tbsp Sage Seasoning, page 218

1 1/2 cups Almond Bread, crumbled, page 166

1 tsp fine grain sea salt

1/2 tsp ground black pepper

2 free-range eggs

1/2 cup Ketchup, page 234

6 tbsps coconut sugar

2 tsps ground dry mustard

Nutrition Facts

Serving Size 6 oz (154g)
Servings Per Container 10

Amount Per Serving

Calories 380   Calories from Fat 240

	% Daily Value*
Total Fat 27g	42%
Saturated Fat 9g	45%
Trans Fat 0g	
Cholesterol 135mg	45%
Sodium 510mg	21%
Total Carbohydrate 12g	4%
Dietary Fiber 1g	4%
Sugars 11g	
Protein 21g	

Vitamin A 4%	•	Vitamin C 6%
Calcium 4%	•	Iron 15%

*Percent Daily Values are based on a 2,000 calorie diet. Your daily values may be higher or lower depending on your calorie needs.

	Calories	2,000	2,500
Total Fat	Less than	65g	80g
Saturated Fat	Less than	20g	25g
Cholesterol	Less than	300mg	300mg
Sodium	Less than	2,400mg	2,400mg
Total Carbohydrate		300g	375g
Dietary Fiber		25g	30g

Calories per gram:
Fat 9 • Carbohydrate 4 • Protein 4

Preheat oven to 375°F.

Prepare Sage Seasoning, Almond Bread Crumbs and Ketchup.

In a large bowl, combine pork, onion, almond bread crumb, sea salt, black pepper and egg; mix well. In a separate bowl, combine whisk ketchup, coconut sugar and dry mustard; mix well.

Add 1/4 cup of the ketchup mixture to the pork mixture; mix well. Roll pork mixture into meatballs and place on a sheet pan lined with aluminum foil. Brush the remaining ketchup on meatballs. Bake for 30 minutes until nicely browned and glazed.

Tip
Do not use regular ketchup in place; loaded with sugars and non-digestible ingredients.

Servings: 6

Target source of Protein, Dietary Fats, B vitamins, Phosphorus, Selenium, Zinc

Supportive of Immune Health

"RED COOKED" PORK & VEGETABLES

2 tbsps coconut oil

2 tsps minced fresh ginger root

2/3 cup coconut aminos

2 tbsps dry sherry

1 tsp crushed fennel seed

3/4 cup water

2 lbs uncured, pastured boneless pork shoulder, cut 1-inch cubes

3-4 tbsps ground ginger

2 tbsps coconut oil

1 cup organic beef broth

3 organic carrots, cut into 1-inch julienne strips

1/2 lb quartered fresh mushroom; try a variety

1 cup green onion, cut into 1-inch length, whites separated

2 tsps arrowroot

2 tbsps water

Nutrition Facts

Serving Size 10oz (290g)
Servings Per Container 8

Amount Per Serving

Calories 320   Calories from Fat 170

% Daily Value*

Total Fat 19g	29%
Saturated Fat 10g	50%
Trans Fat 0g	
Cholesterol 80mg	27%
Sodium 600mg	25%
Total Carbohydrate 15g	5%
Dietary Fiber 4g	16%
Sugars 5g	
Protein 22g	

Vitamin A 100%	•	Vitamin C 90%	
Calcium 6%	•	Iron 10%	

*Percent Daily Values are based on a 2,000 calorie diet. Your daily values may be higher or lower depending on your calorie needs.

		Calories	2,000	2,500
Total Fat	Less than		65g	80g
Saturated Fat	Less than		20g	25g
Cholesterol	Less than		300mg	300mg
Sodium	Less than		2,400mg	2,400mg
Total Carbohydrate			300g	375g
Dietary Fiber			25g	30g

Calories per gram:
Fat 9   •   Carbohydrate 4   •   Protein 4

Prepare Cauliflower Rice and Stir-fry Sauce.

Combine coconut oil, ginger root, and coconut aminos; mix well.

In a medium skillet over high heat, add stir-fry sauce, dry sherry, fennel seed and water; bring to a boil. Reduce heat to low and cover; sauté for 45 minutes, stirring occasionally.

Pork & Vegetables

Rinse and trim excess fat and cut pork shoulder into 1-inch cubes. Rub Pork with ginger. Heat 2 tablespoons of oil in a skillet over medium-high heat. Add the pork and sear on all sides. Drain grease and discard. Return the skillet to the stove over high heat; add beef broth and pork shoulder and bring to a boil. Reduce heat, cover and simmer.

Combine the carrot, mushroom and green onion whites; add to pork skillet, cover and simmer for 30 minutes. Internal temperature of pork should read 160° F, at the thickest part. Stir in stir-fry sauce and green onion tops; cover and cook 3 minutes longer. Blend 2 tablespoons of water with arrowroot. Stir into vegetable mixture; sauté for 1 minute, or until sauce boils and thickens slightly, stirring constantly.

Tip
"Red Cooked" is a slow braising Chinese cooking technique that imparts a red color to the prepared food.

Servings: 4

Target source of Protein, Dietary Fats, Vitamin A, Vitamin B, Vitamin K, Folate, Selenium, Phosphorus, Potassium, Zinc

Supportive of Immune Health

SAVORY APPLE & ONION PORK CHOPS

4 uncured, pastured pork cebter-cut loin chops, cut 1-inch thick, 6 ounces each

3 tbsps extra virgin olive oil, divided

1 cup organic applesauce

1 tsp fine grain sea salt

1/4 tbsp minced fresh rosemary or 1/4 tsp crushed dried rosemary

1/4 tbsp minced fresh thyme or 1/4 tsp crushed dried thyme

1 tbsp water

2 sliced organic red apple, with skin

1/2 cup thinly sliced onion

Nutrition Facts

Serving Size 11 oz (314g)
Servings Per Container 4

Amount Per Serving

Calories 410   Calories from Fat 210

	% Daily Value*
Total Fat 23g	35%
Saturated Fat 7g	35%
Trans Fat 0g	
Cholesterol 90mg	30%
Sodium 1220mg	51%
Total Carbohydrate 19g	6%
Dietary Fiber 3g	12%
Sugars 14g	
Protein 32g	

Vitamin A 0%	•	Vitamin C 70%	
Calcium 4%	•	Iron 6%	

*Percent Daily Values are based on a 2,000 calorie diet. Your daily values may be higher or lower depending on your calorie needs.

		Calories	2,000	2,500
Total Fat	Less than		65g	80g
Saturated Fat	Less than		20g	25g
Cholesterol	Less than		300mg	300mg
Sodium	Less than		2,400mg	2,400mg
Total Carbohydrate			300g	375g
Dietary Fiber			25g	30g

Calories per gram:
Fat 9 • Carbohydrate 4 • Protein 4

Heat 2 tablespoons of oil in a large skillet over medium-high heat. When oil is hot, sear pork chops on both sides, about 3 minutes each side.

Reduce heat to medium; add the applesauce, sea salt, rosemary, thyme and water; cover and sauté for 7-8 minutes. The internal temperature of pork should read 160° F, at the thickest part.

In a separate skillet, heat 1 tablespoon of oil over medium-high heat; sauté the apple and onion for 3-4 minutes, or until apple is softened and begins to golden.

Add applesauce herb mixture to the apple and onion mixture, mix well and serve over pork chops.

Tips
Apples are an excellent compliment to pork dishes.

Serving: 4

Target source of Protein, Vitamin C, Copper, Dietary Fats, Potassium, Zinc

Supportive of Immune Health

SPUNKY ASIAN PORK MEATBALLS

MEATBALLS

2 lbs uncured, pastured ground pork

2 tsps sesame oil

1 cup almond meal

1/2 tsp ground ginger

2 free-range eggs

3 tsps minced garlic

1/2 cup chopped green onion

ASIAN SAUCE

1/4 cup Mother's apple cider vinegar

2 minced garlic clove

2 tbsps coconut aminos

1 tsp sesame oil

1 tsp ground ginger

Preheat oven to 400° F.

Mix together meatball ingredients, in a large bowl; mix until well combined. Shape into 2 oz. balls. Place meatballs on a sheet pan sprayed with cooking oil; bake for 10-12 minutes until meat is cooked through. Internal thermometer should read 160° F, at the thickest part.

In a small bowl, whisk together all of the sauce ingredients, until blended. Remove sheet pan from the oven and let meatballs rest for 5 minutes, covered, before serving.

Servings: 6

Target source of Protein, Dietary Fats, B Vitamins, Iron, Magnesium, Phosphorous, Potassium, Selenium, Zinc

Supportive of Immune Health

"Food Is Essential To Life.
Therefore, Make It Good."

--S. Truett Cathy

SEAFOOD

CRAB CAKES

3 lbs fresh flaked lump crab meat, gently
   picked through and shells removed; not imitation
2 tbsps minced garlic clove
1/2 cup chopped fresh parsley
2-3 free-range eggs, beaten
2 tbsps Sour Cream, page 239
2 tbsps Dijon Mustard, page 228
1 tsp kosher salt
1 tbsp chopped fresh thyme or 1 tsp dried thyme
1 tsp ground organic cayenne
1 cup almond flour
4-6 tbsps Clarified Butter, page 203, divided
Tzatziki Sauce, page 271
1 1/2 cups Sour Cream, page 239
1/4 cup small diced organic cucumber
2 tbsps chopped dill weed

Nutrition Facts
Serving Size 2 (3oz cakes) (268g)
Servings Per Container 8

Amount Per Serving

Calories 420   Calories from Fat 230

% Daily Value*

Total Fat 26g	40%
Saturated Fat 12g	60%
Trans Fat 0g	
Cholesterol 270mg	90%
Sodium 1000mg	42%
Total Carbohydrate 7g	2%
Dietary Fiber 2g	8%
Sugars 2g	
Protein 37g	

Vitamin A 20%	•	Vitamin C 20%	
Calcium 25%	•	Iron 15%	

*Percent Daily Values are based on a 2,000 calorie diet. Your daily values may be higher or lower depending on your calorie needs.

	Calories:	2,000	2,500
Total Fat	Less than	65g	80g
Saturated Fat	Less than	20g	25g
Cholesterol	Less than	300mg	300mg
Sodium	Less than	2,400mg	2,400mg
Total Carbohydrate		300g	375g
Dietary Fiber		25g	30g

Calories per gram:
Fat 9 • Carbohydrate 4 • Protein 4

Prepare Sour Cream, Dijon Mustard, Clarified Butter, and Tzatziki Dipping Sauce.

Allow Tzatziki dipping sauce to chill, covered, in the refrigerator for 45 minutes to infuse flavors.

Heat 2 tablespoons of clarified butter in a skillet over medium heat. Add crab meat and sauté for 3-4 minutes. Add to a medium mixing bowl. Add garlic, parsley, egg, sour cream, Dijon mustard, kosher salt, thyme, cayenne and almond flour; mix well.

Form into four 1/2-inch thick cakes, about 3 ounces each. Place the crab cakes on a plate lined with wax paper. Loosely cover with plastic wrap and refrigerate for 30-45 minutes. Melt 2 tablespoons of clarified butter in a large skillet over medium heat.

When butter is hot, add the crab cakes. Sear 4-5 minutes on each side, until bottom starts browning. Add additional clarified butter, if cakes start sticking. Very carefully lift each crab cake with a metal fish spatula.

Spread or dip into Tzatziki dipping sauce.

Tips
Clarified butter has a high smoke point temperature; great for clean frying.

If you cannot have egg, replace with coconut milk. Let it soak a tad longer before dredging in almond meal.

Servings: 8

Target source of Protein, Dietary Fats, Vitamin A, Vitamin C, Vitamins B3, B6, B12, Folate, Vitamin K, Pantothenic Acid, Magnesium, Phosphorus, Selenium, Zinc

Supportive of Immune Health

CUBAN HALIBUT

4 wild caught Halibut fillet, skin and bone removed, 6 oz each

MARINADE
1 tsp orange zest
1 tsp lime zest
1/2 freshly squeezed lime juice
1/4 tsp fine grain sea salt
1/4 tsp ground black pepper

TOPPING
1 tsp extra virgin olive oil
1/2 cup diced red onion
1 tsp ground cumin
1 tsp dried oregano
1 crushed garlic clove
1/4 tsp fine grain sea salt
1/8 tsp black pepper
3 cups organic spinach leaf
1 orange, sectioned with juice
1 tsp orange zest
1/2 cup chopped cilantro, garnish

Nutrition Facts

Serving Size 6oz (359g)
Servings Per Container 4

Amount Per Serving

Calories 380	Calories from Fat 50

	% Daily Value*
Total Fat 6g	9%
Saturated Fat 1g	5%
Trans Fat 0g	
Cholesterol 190mg	63%
Sodium 410mg	17%
Total Carbohydrate 4g	1%
Dietary Fiber 1g	4%
Sugars 2g	
Protein 72g	

Vitamin A 20%	•	Vitamin C 25%
Calcium 6%	•	Iron 6%

*Percent Daily Values are based on a 2,000 calorie diet. Your daily values may be higher or lower depending on your calorie needs.

	Calories	2,000	2,500
Total Fat	Less than	65g	80g
Saturated Fat	Less than	20g	25g
Cholesterol	Less than	300mg	300mg
Sodium	Less than	2,400mg	2,400mg
Total Carbohydrate		300g	375g
Dietary Fiber		25g	30g

Calories per gram
Fat 9 • Carbohydrate 4 • Protein 4

Preheat oven to broil, 500° F.

Prepare marinade. In a large bowl, mix together orange and lime zest, lime juice, sea salt and black pepper. Add the halibut and pour marinade over halibut and set aside.

Heat the oil in a large skillet over medium heat. Add onion, cumin, oregano, garlic, sea salt and black pepper; sauté for 3 minute until spices release their aroma and the onion begins to soften.

If onion starts becoming too brown, add 3 tablespoons water. Add spinach in batches, cover and sauté for 3 to 4 minutes, until slightly wilted. Gently mix in orange sections, orange juice and orange zest; sauté for an addition 1 minute until heated through.

Place halibut on a sheet pan lined with aluminum foil; broil for 8 minutes. Internal temperature should read 145° F, at the thickest part. Serve over spinach mixture. Garnish with cilantro.

Servings: 4

Target source of Protein, Dietary Fats, Vitamins B3, B6, B12, Vitamin C, Vitamin D, Vitamin K, Magnesium, Phosphorus, Potassium, Selenium

Supportive of Immune Health

FIRECRACKER MEDITERRANEAN SALMON

4 wild caught salmon fillets, 6 oz. each

1 tbsp extra virgin olive oil

1/2 cup chopped organic sun-dried tomato

1/4 cup organic sliced olive, 4 oz can

3/4 tsp Lemon Pepper Seasoning, page 215

3/4 tsp chopped dill weed

1/4 tsp fine grain sea salt

1/4 cup pine nuts

Nutrition Facts

Serving Size 6 oz fillet (232g)
Servings Per Container 4

Amount Per Serving

Calories 520 Calories from Fat 290

	% Daily Value*
Total Fat 32g	49%
Saturated Fat 3.5g	18%
Trans Fat 0g	
Cholesterol 120mg	40%
Sodium 540mg	23%
Total Carbohydrate 11g	4%
Dietary Fiber 2g	8%
Sugars 4g	
Protein 46g	

Vitamin A 2%	•	Vitamin C 6%
Calcium 2%	•	Iron 15%

*Percent Daily Values are based on a 2,000 calorie diet. Your daily values may be higher or lower depending on your calorie needs.

		Calories	2,000	2,500
Total Fat	Less than		65g	80g
Saturated Fat	Less than		20g	25g
Cholesterol	Less than		300mg	300mg
Sodium	Less than		2,400mg	2,400mg
Total Carbohydrate			300g	375g
Dietary Fiber			25g	30g

Calories per gram:
Fat 9 • Carbohydrate 4 • Protein 4

Preheat oven at 400° F.

Prepare Lemon Pepper Seasoning.

In a small bowl, mix together tomato and olive. Rinse salmon, pat dry with a disposable paper towel, and brush with oil. Place the salmon on a sheet pan lined with aluminum foil and sprayed with cooking oil. Sprinkle both sides of fish with lemon pepper, dill and sea salt, both sides. Top with tomato and olive mixture. Fold at the top and secure all sides; seam side up.

Bake for 18-20 minutes until cooked through. Internal temperature should read 145° F, at the thickest part.

Servings: 4

Target source of Protein, Dietary Fats, Omega 3, B Vitamins, Folate, Pantothenic Acid, Copper, Iron, Magnesium, Potassium, Phosphorus, Selenium

Supportive of Immune Health

GINGER DILL GLAZED SALMON

4 salmon fillets, with or without skin, 6 oz each
4 tbsps Mother's apple cider vinegar; plus1 tsp
1 1/2 tsps chopped dill weed
1 tbsp extra virgin olive oil
1 1/2 tsps ground ginger
1/4 tsp fine sea salt
1 1/2 tbsps sesame oil
2 1/4 tbsps organic ginger spread
Ginger-Dill Glaze Sauce, page 263

Preheat oven to 400°F.

Prepare Ginger-Dill Glaze Sauce.

In a bowl, combine apple cider vinegar, dill, oil, ginger, sea salt, sesame oil and organic ginger spread. Mix to incorporate and set aside.

Carefully rinse salmon and place on a baking sheet pan, sprayed with cooking oil. Lightly salt and pepper both sides. Brush ginger-dill glaze over salmon to coat. Place glazed salmon in the refrigerator for 10 minutes to set.

Bake for 12-15 minutes, more or less depending on each fillets thickness. Internal temperature should read 145° F, at the thickest area. Remove the Salmon and rest for 5 minutes; loosely covered. Scrape off excess fat sitting on Salmon, with a paring knife. Add more glaze, if you desire.

Tip
Salmon will soak in sea salt, so add a little at a time for even coverage. Salmon should be cooked skin down, if applicable.

Servings: 4

Target source of Protein, Omega 3 Fat, Fatty Acids

Supportive of Immune Health

GRILLED TUNA STEAKS WITH FRESH SWEET BASIL

REFER TO HOW TO COOK TUNA, page 133

6 tuna steaks, 6 oz each

3 tbsps extra virgin olive oil

3 tbsps chopped fresh basil or 3 tsps dried basil

1 tsp fine grain sea salt

1 tsp ground black pepper

Nutrition Facts

Serving Size 6 oz fillet (180g)
Servings Per Container 6

Amount Per Serving

Calories 370   Calories from Fat 160

	% Daily Value^
Total Fat 18g	28%
Saturated Fat 3.5g	18%
Trans Fat 0g	
Cholesterol 85mg	28%
Sodium 470mg	20%
Total Carbohydrate 0g	0%
Dietary Fiber 0g	0%
Sugars 0g	
Protein 51g	

Vitamin A 90%	•	Vitamin C 0%
Calcium 2%	•	Iron 15%

*Percent Daily Values are based on a 2,000 calorie diet. Your daily values may be higher or lower depending on your calorie needs.

	Calories:	2,000	2,500
Total Fat	Less than	65g	80g
Saturated Fat	Less than	20g	25g
Cholesterol	Less than	300mg	300mg
Sodium	Less than	2,400mg	2,400mg
Total Carbohydrate		300g	375g
Dietary Fiber		25g	30g

Calories per gram:
Fat 9 • Carbohydrate 4 • Protein 4

Preheat the grill to medium-high heat. Brush the rack with cooking oil.

Mix basil, sea salt and black pepper and season tuna steaks on both sides. Place the tuna on grill for 4-5 minutes, each side, and lid down. Internal temperature should read 145° F, at the thickest part; flesh needs to be opaque and separate easily with a fork.

Tip
Alternatively, you can preheat oven to broil. Place sheet pan 4-inches from the heat and cook for 4-5 minutes each side; no pink.

Servings: 6

Target source of Protein, Dietary Fats, Omega 3, Vitamin A, B Vitamins, Pantothenic Acid, Copper, Iron, Magnesium, Phosphorus, Potassium, Selenium

Supportive of Immune Health

SPICY PINEAPPLE GLAZED COD FILLET

2 lbs wild caught cod fillet, or other white fish

2 tbsps extra virgin olive oil

1 tsp kosher salt, divided

1 tsp ground black pepper

3/4 cup organic pineapple preserve

1 cup small diced fresh pineapple

2 tbsps Mother's apple cider vinegar

2 tsps minced fresh ginger root

2 minced garlic clove

1 tsp ground organic cayenne

Nutrition Facts

Serving Size 5 oz (229g)
Servings Per Container 6

Amount Per Serving

Calories 300   Calories from Fat 35

% Daily Value*

Total Fat 3.5g — 5%

Saturated Fat 0.5g — 3%

Trans Fat 0g

Cholesterol 85mg — 28%

Sodium 440mg — 18%

Total Carbohydrate 31g — 10%

Dietary Fiber 1g — 4%

Sugars 27g

Protein 35g

Vitamin A 4% • Vitamin C 25%

Calcium 2% • Iron 6%

*Percent Daily Values are based on a 2,000 calorie diet. Your daily values may be higher or lower depending on your calorie needs.

	Calories	2,000	2,500
Total Fat	Less than	65g	80g
Saturated Fat	Less than	20g	25g
Cholesterol	Less than	300mg	300mg
Sodium	Less than	2,400mg	2,400mg
Total Carbohydrate		300g	375g
Dietary Fiber		25g	30g

Calories per gram
Fat 9 • Carbohydrate 4 • Protein 4

Preheat oven to broil, 500° F.

Place fillets on a sheet pan coated with cooking oil; sprinkle with 1/2 teaspoon kosher salt and black pepper on both sides. In a bowl, combine pineapple preserve, pineapple, vinegar, ginger, garlic, 1/2 teaspoon kosher salt and cayenne; spoon oil over both sides of fillet.

Broil 4-6 inches from the heat for 5 minutes. Baste with half of the preserve glaze. Broil for an additional 5-7minutes, or until fish flakes. Baste with remaining glaze and serve.

Servings: 4

Target source of Protein, Vitamins B3, B6, B12, Vitamin C, Vitamin D, Magnesium, Manganese, Phosphorus, Selenium, Zinc

Supportive of Immune Health

SCALLOPS AND VEGETABLES OVER ZUCCHINI NOODLES

2 1/2 lbs large wild caught scallop or small bay scallop

12 ozs Zucchini Noodle, page 323

3-5 tbsps Clarified Butter, page 203, divided

2 chopped celery stalk, about 3/4 cup

1 julienned red bell pepper, seeds and ribs removed

2 julienned organic carrots

3 diagonally cut green onions, cut on a bias

1/2 cup freshly orange juice, about 2 medium oranges

1 tsp grated orange zest

1 1/2 tbsps red pepper flake

1/4 cup chopped parsley, garnish

Nutrition Facts

Serving Size 5 oz scallops (11 oz total weight) (332g)
Servings Per Container 6

Amount Per Serving

Calories 220   Calories from Fat 60

	% Daily Value*
Total Fat 6g	9%
Saturated Fat 3.5g	18%
Trans Fat 0g	
Cholesterol 60mg	20%
Sodium 880mg	37%
Total Carbohydrate 15g	5%
Dietary Fiber 2g	8%
Sugars 5g	
Protein 24g	

Vitamin A 110%	•	Vitamin C 80%
Calcium 4%	•	Iron 8%

*Percent Daily Values are based on a 2,000 calorie diet. Your daily values may be higher or lower depending on your calorie needs.

	Calories	2,000	2,500
Total Fat	Less than	65g	80g
Saturated Fat	Less than	20g	25g
Cholesterol	Less than	300mg	300mg
Sodium	Less than	2,400mg	2,400mg
Total Carbohydrate		300g	375g
Dietary Fiber		25g	30g

Calories per gram
Fat 9 • Carbohydrate 4 • Protein 4

Prepare Zucchini Noodle and Clarified Butter.

Heat 2 tablespoons of clarified butter in a large skillet over medium-high heat. Add celery, pepper, carrot and green onion; sauté until crisp tender, about 5 minutes.

Slice scallop in thirds, or use whole bay scallops. Add 1 tablespoon of clarified butter and reduce heat to medium. Add scallop: sauté until opaque, about 2-3minutes. Be careful not to overcook or they become tough and rubbery. Add orange juice, orange zest and pepper flake; sauté an additional 2 minutes.

In a separate skillet, heat 1 tablespoon of clarified butter over medium heat. Add zucchini noodle; heat for 2 minute, stirring often. Reduce heat to low, and cover to stay heated.

Plate cooked zucchini noodles and top with vegetable mixture, and then with scallop. Sprinkle with a parsley and serve.

Tip
Freeze fully cooked in a food saver bag.

Servings: 6

Target source of Protein, Vitamin A, Vitamin C, Vitamins B6, B12, Folate, Vitamin K, Phosphorus, Potassium, Selenium, Zinc

Supportive of Immune Health

SWEET POTATO SALMON CAKES

2 lbs wild caught salmon
3 sweet potatoes, peeled and mashed
2 pureed onion
3 tbsps coconut milk, full fat (in a can)
3 tbsps minced cilantro
3-4 tbsps Clarified Butter, page 203
2 cups almond meal, more if needed
1 1/2 tbsps freshly squeezed lime juice
1/2 tsp fine grain sea salt, to taste
1/2 tsp ground black pepper, to taste
Tzatziki Sauce, optional page 271

Nutrition Facts

Serving Size 2 (4oz) patties (226g)
Servings Per Container 8

Amount Per Serving

Calories 480	Calories from Fat 270

	% Daily Value*
Total Fat 30g	46%
Saturated Fat 7g	35%
Trans Fat 0g	
Cholesterol 95mg	32%
Sodium 240mg	10%
Total Carbohydrate 18g	6%
Dietary Fiber 5g	20%
Sugars 5g	
Protein 36g	

Vitamin A 170%	•	Vitamin C 20%
Calcium 10%	•	Iron 15%

*Percent Daily Values are based on a 2,000 calorie diet. Your daily values may be higher or lower depending on your calorie needs.

	Calories	2,000	2,500
Total Fat	Less than	65g	80g
Saturated Fat	Less than	20g	25g
Cholesterol	Less than	300mg	300mg
Sodium	Less than	2,400mg	2,400mg
Total Carbohydrate		300g	375g
Dietary Fiber		25g	30g

Calories per gram:
Fat 9 • Carbohydrate 4 • Protein 4

Preheat oven to 400° F.

Prepare Clarified Butter.

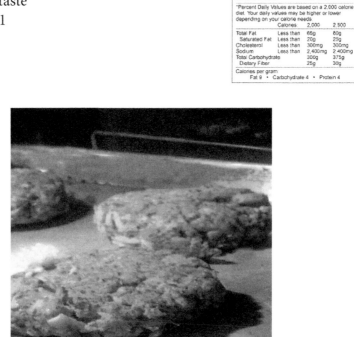

Coat a sheet pan with cooking oil. Place salmon, skin down and cook for about 13-15 minutes until cooked throughout. Internal temperature should read 145° F, at the thickest part. Let cool, remove skin and flake with a fork. Discard skin.

Fill a saucepan with water and add sweet potato to a saucepan; bring to a boil over high heat. Remove sweet potato and strain water, when sweet potato is tender to touch with fork, about 10-15 minutes. Mash sweet potato and place in a large mixing bowl.

Chop onion and place in a food processor to slightly puree. Combine flaked fish, mashed sweet potato, onion, coconut milk full fat, cilantro, lime juice, sea salt and black pepper; mix well.

Using your hands or a scoop, take about 3-4 ounces of mixture and roll into a ball. Repeat with all the mixture. Place balls on a sheet pan lined with parchment paper. Place in the refrigerator for a minimum of 30 minutes to set. When salmon balls are set, flatten and make into patty cakes.

Prepare two bowls; egg in one, and almond meal in another. Dredge the salmon cake through the egg mixture, covering all surface, and then through the almond meal.

Heat 2 tablespoons of clarified butter in the skillet over medium-high heat. Transfer salmon patties to the hot butter and sear both sides, for about 1-2 minutes on each side. Remember the salmon is already cooked; you do not want to overcook. Add more butter as needed to prevent sticking.

Let salmon cakes cool slightly and serve.

Servings: 4

Target source of Protein, Dietary Fats, Omega 3, Dietary Fiber, Vitamin A, B Vitamins, Pantothenic Acid, Copper, Magnesium, Phosphorus, Selenium

Supportive of Immune Health

132.

HOW TO COOK TUNA

Preheat the oven to 350° F.

Bake the tuna fillets.

Internal Temperatures
Rare - 120° F, four minutes per inch of thickness
Medium-Rare - 130° F, five minutes per inch of thickness
Medium - 140° F, six minutes per inch of thickness

VEGGIE & CASSEROLE

CHICKEN AND MUSHROOM CASSEROLE

2 lbs free-range, pastured chicken breast, cut into 1-inch cubes

1 tbsp of extra virgin olive oil

2 1/2 cups sliced fresh mushrooms; variety

1/4 cup chopped organic fresh pineapple chunks

1/2 cup diced organic green bell pepper

1/4 cup chopped green onion

1 cup pineapple juice

1 tbsp arrowroot powder

1 1/4 tsps fine grain sea salt

1 1/4 tsps ground black pepper

1/2 tsp ground ginger

1 tbsp of extra virgin olive oil

3 chopped organic carrots, peeled

Nutrition Facts		
Serving Size 8oz (250g)		
Servings Per Container 8		
Amount Per Serving		
Calories 180	Calories from Fat 15	
		% Daily Value*
Total Fat 1.5g		2%
Saturated Fat 0g		0%
Trans Fat 0g		
Cholesterol 65mg		22%
Sodium 460mg		19%
Total Carbohydrate 14g		5%
Dietary Fiber 2g		8%
Sugars 9g		
Protein 27g		
Vitamin A 80%	•	Vitamin C 80%
Calcium 2%	•	Iron 8%

*Percent Daily Values are based on a 2,000 calorie diet. Your daily values may be higher or lower depending on your calorie needs.

		Calories	2,000	2,500
Total Fat	Less than		65g	80g
Saturated Fat	Less than		20g	25g
Cholesterol	Less than		300mg	300mg
Sodium	Less than		2,400mg	2,400mg
Total Carbohydrate			300g	375g
Dietary Fiber			25g	30g

Calories per gram:
Fat 9 • Carbohydrate 4 • Protein 4

Preheat oven to 350° F.

Slice mushrooms and set aside. Rinse chicken. Heat 1 tablespoon of oil in a skillet over medium-high heat. Once the skillet is hot, sear the chicken on all sides. Remove the skillet and let chicken rest, covered for 3 minutes. Transfer to a 9 X 13 casserole dish. Internal temperature of chicken should read 165° F, at the thickest part.

Sprinkle mushroom, pineapple, bell pepper and green onion over chicken. Combine pineapple liquid with arrowroot, sea salt, black pepper and ginger; mix well. Pour the mixture over chicken and cover tightly with aluminum foil. Bake for 45 minutes until the chicken is tender.

Reheat the same skillet over medium-high heat. Add 1 tablespoon of oil and sauté carrot until crisp tender, about 3 to 5 minutes. Serve chicken surrounded by carrots.

Tips
Optional: purchase a 20 oz can of unsweetened organic pineapple; freeze the leftovers. Try a variety of mushrooms for more flavors. (Cremini, Shitake, Button, Portobello, Oyster)*

Servings: 6

Target source of Protein, Vitamin A, Vitamin C

Supportive of Immune Health

EASY SWEET POTATO VEGGIE BURGERS WITH AVOCADO

2 1/2 cups roughly mashed sweet potato

1 cup organic chopped green (spinach or kale)

2/3 cup almond meal

1 free-range egg, lightly beaten

1 1/2 tsps ground smoked paprika

1 tsp onion powder

1 tsp fine grain sea salt

1/2 tsp ground black pepper

1/8 tsp ground cumin

2/3 cup Sour Cream, page 239

2 squeezed Roasted Garlic clove, page 238

1 tsp maple syrup, grade B

1/8 tsp fine grain sea salt

1/8 tsp ground black pepper

2-3 tbsps coconut oil

1 sliced avocado, garnish

1 tbsp freshly squeezed lemon juice; to prevent browning

Nutrition Facts		
Serving Size 4oz (130g)		
Servings Per Container 8		
Amount Per Serving		
Calories 230	Calories from Fat 130	
		% Daily Value*
Total Fat 15g		**23%**
Saturated Fat 6g		**30%**
Trans Fat 0g		
Cholesterol 40mg		**13%**
Sodium 370mg		**15%**
Total Carbohydrate 19g		**6%**
Dietary Fiber 4g		**16%**
Sugars 6g		
Protein 6g		
Vitamin A 250%	•	Vitamin C 25%
Calcium 8%	•	Iron 8%

*Percent Daily Values are based on a 2,000 calorie diet. Your daily values may be higher or lower depending on your calorie needs.

	Calories:	2,000	2,500
Total Fat	Less than	65g	80g
Saturated Fat	Less than	20g	25g
Cholesterol	Less than	300mg	300mg
Sodium	Less than	2,400mg	2,400mg
Total Carbohydrate		300g	375g
Dietary Fiber		25g	30g

Calories per gram:
Fat 9 • Carbohydrate 4 • Protein 4

Preheat oven to 400° F.

Prepare Sour Cream and Roasted Garlic.

Peel the sweet potato and poke with a fork on all sides. Place on a sheet pan lined with aluminum foil. Bake for 45 minutes until tender. Combine sweet potato, spinach, almond meal, egg, paprika, onion powder, sea salt, black pepper and cumin in a medium bowl; mash and mix well. Place bowl in the refrigerator for 20-30 minutes to chill.

Add prepared sour cream, squeezed roasted garlic clove, maple syrup, sea salt and black pepper in a blender or food processor; blend until smooth.

Heat 2 tablespoons of coconut oil in a large skillet over medium heat. Form the sweet potato mixture into 4 burgers. Place the burgers in the skill; sauté for 5 minutes or until, carefully flipping with a metal spatula. Sweet potato is naturally sticky, so add more oil as needed to keep the skillet from drying out.

Slice avocado and top with Roasted Garlic and Sour Cream mixture.

Tip
Try replacing with a large Portobello mushroom, washed with stem and gill removed.

Servings: 6-8

Target source of Vitamins B1, B2, B3, B6, B12, Vitamin A, Folate, Pantothenic Acid, Fiber, Molybdenum, Manganese

Supportive of Immune, Detoxification and Gut Health

MASHED CREAMY SQUASH & KALE CASSEROLE

1 cup thinly sliced onion

4-5 tbsps extra virgin olive oil, divided

1 lb butternut squash peeled, cut into 1-inch cubes

2 sweet potatoes, peeled, cut into 1-inch cubes

1/8 tsp fine grain sea salt

1/8 tsp ground black pepper

8 cups kale

Nutrition Facts

Serving Size 1/2 cup (130g)
Servings Per Container 8

Amount Per Serving

Calories 180   Calories from Fat 120

	% Daily Value*
Total Fat 14g	22%
Saturated Fat 2g	10%
Trans Fat 0g	
Cholesterol 0mg	0%
Sodium 20mg	1%
Total Carbohydrate 15g	5%
Dietary Fiber 4g	16%
Sugars 4g	
Protein 2g	

Vitamin A 270%	•	Vitamin C 60%
Calcium 6%	•	Iron 4%

*Percent Daily Values are based on a 2,000 calorie diet. Your daily values may be higher or lower depending on your calorie needs.

	Calories	2,000	2,500
Total Fat	Less than	65g	80g
Saturated Fat	Less than	20g	25g
Cholesterol	Less than	300mg	300mg
Sodium	Less than	2,400mg	2,400mg
Total Carbohydrate		300g	375g
Dietary Fiber		25g	30g

Calories per gram
Fat 9 • Carbohydrate 4 • Protein 4

Preheat oven to 375° F.

Heat 2 tablespoons of oil in a skillet over medium-high heat. Add onion; sauté for 2 minutes, then reduce heat to medium-low and sauté for an additional 15 minutes. Do not brown onions.

Meanwhile, place squash and sweet potato in sprayed baking dish, cover and bake for 25-30 minutes until tender. Chop kale into 1-inch pieces and set aside. In a large bowl, mash sweet potato, squash and the remaining 3 tablespoons of extra virgin olive oil until smooth and creamy.

When onion is finished, add sea salt, black pepper and kale to the skillet. Cover and sauté over medium heat until kale is wilted, about 5 minutes. Add squash and kale mixtures together and bake in the oven for 10 minutes until browning on top.

Plate squash and sweet potato mash and top with onion and kale mixture.

Servings: 6

Target source of Dietary Fats, Fiber, Vitamin A, Vitamin C, Vitamin K, Copper, Manganese, Selenium

Supportive of Immune Health

144.

PESTO EGGPLANT

2 small sliced eggplant, 1-inch slices, with skin or without

2 tbsps The Best Pesto Sauce, page 268

1 cup small diced organic cherry tomato, seeded and juice
  removed

1/4 tsp fine sea salt

1 tsp ground black pepper

1/4 cup chopped fresh parsley

2 cups almond meal

Nutrition Facts

Serving Size 7 oz (189g)
Servings Per Container 8

Amount Per Serving

Calories 220   Calories from Fat 140

	% Daily Value*
Total Fat 16g	25%
Saturated Fat 1.5g	8%
Trans Fat 0g	
Cholesterol 0mg	0%
Sodium 100mg	4%
Total Carbohydrate 15g	5%
Dietary Fiber 7g	28%
Sugars 6g	
Protein 8g	

Vitamin A 6%	•	Vitamin C 15%	
Calcium 8%	•	Iron 8%	

*Percent Daily Values are based on a 2,000 calorie diet. Your daily values may be higher or lower depending on your calorie needs.

		Calories	2,000	2,500
Total Fat	Less than		65g	80g
Saturated Fat	Less than		20g	25g
Cholesterol	Less than		300mg	300mg
Sodium	Less than		2,400mg	2,400mg
Total Carbohydrate			300g	375g
Dietary Fiber			25g	30g

Calories per gram
Fat 9 • Carbohydrate 4 • Protein 4

Preheat the oven to 350°F.

Prepare The Best Pesto sauce.

Place the eggplant slices on a lightly sprayed sheet pan. Position the eggplant with no sides touching. Spread a thin layer of the best pesto sauce over each eggplant slice. Sprinkle top with tomato, sea salt and black pepper. Garnish with sprinkled almond meal and parsley. Bake for 15 minutes until the eggplant is soft and almond meal is lightly golden.

Servings: 8

Target source of Vitamin K, Vitamin C, Potassium, Magnesium, Molybdenum, Manganese, Iron, Dietary Fats, Dietary Fiber, Protein

Supportive of Immune and Gut Health

SHEPHERD'S CAULIFLOWER MASH PIE

2 lbs grass-fed ground beef or 93/7 lean ground beef

1 cauliflower head, cut into florets

6 tbsps extra virgin olive oil, divided

3/4 cup organic beef stock, divided

3/4 cup coarsely chopped onion

1 cup diced organic carrot

1/4 tsp fine grain sea salt, to taste

1/4 tsp ground black pepper, to taste

1 tbsp fresh thyme or 1 tsp dried thyme

1 tbsp fresh rosemary or 1 tsp dried rosemary

1/2 tsp ground paprika

Nutrition Facts

Serving Size 8oz (228g)
Servings Per Container 8

Amount Per Serving

Calories 210   Calories from Fat 130

	% Daily Value*
Total Fat 15g	**23%**
Saturated Fat 3g	**15%**
Trans Fat 0g	
Cholesterol 30mg	**10%**
Sodium 210mg	**9%**
Total Carbohydrate 9g	**3%**
Dietary Fiber 3g	**12%**
Sugars 3g	
Protein 14g	

Vitamin A 60%	•	Vitamin C 90%
Calcium 4%	•	Iron 10%

*Percent Daily Values are based on a 2,000 calorie diet. Your daily values may be higher or lower depending on your calorie needs.

	Calories	2,000	2,500
Total Fat	Less than	65g	80g
Saturated Fat	Less than	20g	25g
Cholesterol	Less than	300mg	300mg
Sodium	Less than	2,400mg	2,400mg
Total Carbohydrate		300g	375g
Dietary Fiber		25g	30g

Calories per gram:
Fat 9 • Carbohydrate 4 • Protein 4

Preheat oven to 400° F.

Boil the cauliflower in a pot of salted water until crisp tender.

Drain and mash with 2 tablespoons of oil and 3 tablespoons of stock. Use more or less stock to control the consistency of the mash; season with sea salt and black pepper, to taste.

Heat 3 tablespoons of oil in a skillet over a medium-low heat; sauté the onion, about 5 minutes. Add the ground beef; sauté for 5 minutes. Add the diced carrots; sauté for 5 minutes.

Pour in the remaining beef stock; and then add with sea salt, black pepper, thyme and rosemary. Simmer uncovered for about 5 minutes. Spread the cooked beef mixture in a sprayed 9-inch baking dish. Gently spread the cauliflower mash on top.

Drizzle the remaining 1 tablespoons of oil on top of the mash. Bake for 30 minutes. Garnish with sprinkled paprika.

Servings: 8

Target source of Protein, Dietary Fats, Dietary Fiber, Omega 3 Fats, Vitamin A, Vitamins B1, B2, B3, B6, B12, Vitamin C, Folate, Vitamin K, Iron, Manganese, Potassium, Zinc

ZUCCHINI STRIP LASAGNA

1 1/2 lbs grass-fed ground hamburger or 93/7 lean
    ground beef

1 diced organic red onion

4 crushed garlic cloves

2 tbsps extra virgin olive oil

1 1/2 cups pastured ground turkey

2 tbsps fresh oregano or 2 tsps dried oregano

2 tbsps fresh basil or 2 tsps dried basil

1/2 tsp ground cayenne

1/2 tsp fine grain sea salt

7 oz can organic tomato paste

10 fresh diced organic tomato

1 cup sliced organic black olives

Nutrition Facts

Serving Size 2 cup (514g)
Servings Per Container 6

Amount Per Serving

Calories 370	Calories from Fat 150

	% Daily Value*
Total Fat 17g	26%
Saturated Fat 3.5g	18%
Trans Fat 0g	
Cholesterol 90mg	30%
Sodium 590mg	25%
Total Carbohydrate 21g	7%
Dietary Fiber 6g	24%
Sugars 11g	
Protein 38g	

Vitamin A 35%	•	Vitamin C 80%
Calcium 8%	•	Iron 30%

*Percent Daily Values are based on a 2,000 calorie diet. Your daily values may be higher or lower depending on your calorie needs.

	Calories	2,000	2,500
Total Fat	Less than	65g	80g
Saturated Fat	Less than	20g	25g
Cholesterol	Less than	300mg	300mg
Sodium	Less than	2,400mg	2,400mg
Total Carbohydrate		300g	375g
Dietary Fiber		25g	30g

Calories per gram
Fat 9 • Carbohydrate 4 • Protein 4

Preheat the oven to 350° F.

Heat 2 tablespoons of oil in a large skillet over medium heat; sauté onion and garlic, for about 3 minutes. Add the beef and turkey; sauté for 5-7 minutes until cooked through, no pink. Add oregano, basil, cayenne, sea salt, oil, tomato paste, tomato and black olive; mix well, stirring occasionally.

Layer zucchini and beef mixture in a baking pan sprayed with cooking spray. Bake for 20 minutes.

Servings: 6

Target source of Protein, Dietary Fiber, Dietary Fats, Omega 3 fat, Vitamin A, Vitamins B1, B2, B3, B6, B12, Vitamin C, Folate, Vitamin K, Iron, Zinc, Manganese, Potassium, Molybdenum

Supportive of Immune and Detoxification Health

139.

DESSERT

ALMOND HONEY SOP

1 cup almond butter

2/3 cup whipped local raw honey

In a food processor, add honey and blend until honey is whipped and has a creamier texture.

Add almond butter and mix thoroughly. Use a spatula, scrap honey mixture into a bowl and serve.

Yield: 1 2/3 cups

Target source of Dietary Fiber, Vitamin C, Vitamins B1, B6, Folate, Copper, Manganese, Potassium, Dietary Fats

Supportive of Immune and Gut Health

Nutrition Facts
Serving Size 2oz (60g)
Servings Per Container 8

Amount Per Serving

Calories 280　Calories from Fat 160

% Daily Value*

Total Fat 18g — 28%
Saturated Fat 2g — 10%
Trans Fat 0g

Cholesterol 0mg — 0%
Sodium 75mg — 3%
Total Carbohydrate 29g — 10%
Dietary Fiber 3g — 12%
Sugars 23g

Protein 7g

Vitamin A 0% • Vitamin C 0%
Calcium 10% • Iron 6%

APPLE CRISP

4 sliced large organic apples, peeled and cored

3/4 cup coconut sugar

1/2 cup coconut flour, sifted

3/4 cup almond flour

3/4 tsp ground cinnamon

3/4 tbsp grated fresh nutmeg or 3/4 tsp ground nutmeg

1/3 cup Clarified Butter, page 203, room temperature

Nutrition Facts
Serving Size 1 cup (168g)
Servings Per Container 6

Amount Per Serving

Calories 380　Calories from Fat 190

% Daily Value*

Total Fat 21g — 32%
Saturated Fat 10g — 50%
Trans Fat 0g

Cholesterol 35mg — 12%
Sodium 65mg — 3%
Total Carbohydrate 46g — 15%
Dietary Fiber 6g — 24%
Sugars 36g

Protein 5g

Vitamin A 10% • Vitamin C 20%
Calcium 4% • Iron 4%

APPLE CRISP

Preheat oven to 350° F.

Prepare Clarified Butter.

Lay the apples in a baking dish sprayed with cooking oil. Mix the coconut sugar, coconut flour, almond flour, cinnamon, and nutmeg together. Pour evenly on top of the apples. Drop dots of clarified butter over the dry mixture. Bake for 25 minutes. Remove from the oven, let set to cool slightly, and serve.

Servings: 4

Target source of Vitamin C, Vitamin A, Magnesium, Potassium, Dietary Fiber, Dietary Fats

Supportive of Gut Health

BROILED PINEAPPLE

1 sliced whole pineapple

10 each fresh organic cherry

3 tbsps coconut sugar

1 tbsp local raw honey

1 1/2 tbsps melted Clarified Butter, page 203

1/2 tsp ground cinnamon

Nutrition Facts
Serving Size 12 1/2 oz (2 slices)
(358g)
Servings Per Container 5

Amount Per Serving

Calories 260   Calories from Fat 45

% Daily Value*

Total Fat 5g		8%
Saturated Fat 3g		15%
Trans Fat 0g		
Cholesterol 15mg		5%
Sodium 15mg		1%
Total Carbohydrate 56g		19%
Dietary Fiber 5g		20%
Sugars 45g		

Protein 2g

Vitamin A 8%	•	Vitamin C 580%
Calcium 4%	•	Iron 6%

*Percent Daily Values are based on a 2,000 calorie diet. Your daily values may be higher or lower depending on your calorie needs

		Calories	2,000	2,500
Total Fat	Less than		65g	80g
Saturated Fat	Less than		20g	25g
Cholesterol	Less than		300mg	300mg
Sodium	Less than		2,400mg	2,400mg
Total Carbohydrate			300g	375g
Dietary Fiber			25g	30g

Calories per gram:
Fat 9 • Carbohydrate 4 • Protein 4

Preheat oven to Broil, 500° F.

Prepare Clarified Butter.

Peel, core and slice pineapple rings 1-inch thick; about 10 slices. Lay pineapple rings on a sheet pan lined with aluminum foil and allow the edges to touch.

Combine coconut sugar and honey; mix well. With a fork, drizzle the honey mixture over each ring. Then drizzle the melted clarified butter and sprinkle with cinnamon. Place a cherry in the center.

Place the sheet pan 5 inches from broiler and broil for 5 minutes or until topping is bubbly.

Servings: 5

Target source of Dietary Fiber, Vitamin C, Vitamins B1, B6, Folate, Copper, Manganese, Potassium, Dietary Fats

Supportive of Immune and Gut Health

CARROT CAKE TREATS

1 cup maple syrup, grade B

1 tbsp ground cinnamon

1 cup melted coconut oil

1 cup shredded organic carrot

1 tsp baking soda

10 free-range eggs, beaten

10 chopped dates, about 2/3 cup

3/4 cup coconut flour, sifted

1 tsp fine grain sea salt

1 tsp pure vanilla extract

Nutrition Facts
Serving Size 2 oz (1 piece) (58g)
Servings Per Container 36

Amount Per Serving

Calories 210	Calories from Fat 150

	% Daily Value*
Total Fat 17g	26%
Saturated Fat 11g	55%
Trans Fat 0g	
Cholesterol 80mg	27%
Sodium 140mg	6%
Total Carbohydrate 12g	4%
Dietary Fiber 2g	8%
Sugars 9g	
Protein 3g	

Vitamin A 10%	•	Vitamin C 0%
Calcium 4%	•	Iron 2%

*Percent Daily Values are based on a 2,000 calorie
diet. Your daily values may be higher or lower
depending on your calorie needs.

	Calories	2,000	2,500
Total Fat	Less than	65g	80g
Saturated Fat	Less than	20g	25g
Cholesterol	Less than	300mg	300mg
Sodium	Less than	2,400mg	2,400mg
Total Carbohydrate		300g	375g
Dietary Fiber		25g	30g

Calories per gram:
Fat 9 • Carbohydrate 4 • Protein 4

TOPPING OPTIONS

1/2 cup unsweetened coconut flakes, toasted

Local raw honey for dipping

Preheat oven to 325° F.

Shred carrots and place in a zip lock bag. Pour maple syrup over carrots; marinade for 1 hour.

Sift coconut flour into mixing bowl, and then add cinnamon, sea salt and baking soda. Be sure to pinch any baking soda clumps to powder. In a small bowl, mix dates with 1 tablespoon of maple syrup; mix well.

In a blender or food processor, blend egg, vanilla, coconut oil and date mix. Slowly add in flour mixture; blend to thick cake consistency.

Remove carrots from refrigerator and place in a strainer for 3-5 minutes, to drain excess maple syrup from carrots. Lightly fold shredded carrots into batter; mix well.

Pour batter into greased mini muffin pan or a loaf pan. Place 1 walnut piece on top of raw batter in the center. Bake 30 minutes. Choice of topping or eat them plain; either way, they are delicious!

Tips
You can toast 3/4 cup of coconut flakes in a skillet over medium heat; stirring often. Lay out on a paper towel to cool.

Lightly brush each cake with maple syrup, and then sprinkle unsweetened coconut flakes; not too much maple or they will become soggy and overly sweet.

You can use grass fed cream cheese and make a glaze to spread on top.

Servings: 36

Target source of Dietary Fats, Vitamin A, Vitamins B12, B2, Calcium, Manganese

Supportive of Immune Health

FRESH BERRY MEDLEY

1/2 cup sliced organic strawberry

1/2 cup raspberry

1/2 cup organic blueberry, domestic

1/2 cup blackberry

1 freshly squeezed lemon juice

Nutrition Facts
Serving Size 1/2 cup (81g)
Servings Per Container 4

Amount Per Serving	
Calories 35	Calories from Fat 0

	% Daily Value*
Total Fat 0g	0%
Saturated Fat 0g	0%
Trans Fat 0g	
Cholesterol 0mg	0%
Sodium 0mg	0%
Total Carbohydrate 9g	3%
Dietary Fiber 2g	8%
Sugars 4g	
Protein 1g	

Vitamin A 2%	•	Vitamin C 40%
Calcium 2%	•	Iron 2%

*Percent Daily Values are based on a 2,000 calorie diet. Your daily values may be higher or lower depending on your calorie needs.

	Calories:	2,000	2,500
Total Fat	Less than	65g	80g
Saturated Fat	Less than	20g	25g
Cholesterol	Less than	300mg	300mg
Sodium	Less than	2,400mg	2,400mg
Total Carbohydrate		300g	375g
Dietary Fiber		25g	30g

Calories per gram
Fat 9 • Carbohydrate 4 • Protein 4

Lightly toss all ingredients together and serve.

Servings: 4

Target source of Dietary Fiber, Vitamin C, Vitamin K, Manganese

Supportive of Immune Health

GINGER-FRUIT COMPOTE

3/4 cup of water

1/2 cup coconut sugar

4 tsps freshly squeezed lemon juice

1 tbsp snipped crystallized ginger

1/2 cup diced kiwi fruits, peeled

1/2 cup orange, sectioned

1/2 cup chopped organic apple

1/2 cup sliced bananas

1/2 cup raspberries

1/2 cup organic blueberries, domestic

1/2 cup organic seedless red grapes

Nutrition Facts

Serving Size 5oz (138g)
Servings Per Container 6

Amount Per Serving

Calories 110	Calories from Fat 0

% Daily Value*

Total Fat 0g	0%
Saturated Fat 0g	0%
Trans Fat 0g	
Cholesterol 0mg	0%
Sodium 30mg	1%
Total Carbohydrate 32g	11%
Dietary Fiber 2g	8%
Sugars 26g	
Protein 1g	

Vitamin A 0%	•	Vitamin C 50%
Calcium 2%	•	Iron 2%

*Percent Daily Values are based on a 2,000 calorie diet. Your daily values may be higher or lower depending on your calorie needs.

	Calories	2,000	2,500
Total Fat	Less than	65g	80g
Saturated Fat	Less than	20g	25g
Cholesterol	Less than	300mg	300mg
Sodium	Less than	2,400mg	2,400mg
Total Carbohydrate		300g	375g
Dietary Fiber		25g	30g

Calories per gram
Fat 9 • Carbohydrate 4 • Protein 4

In a medium saucepan, combine water, coconut sugar, lemon juice and ginger; mix well. Bring to a boil; sauté until they are golden brown, stirring frequently with a wooden spoon. Reduce heat, cover and simmer for 5 minutes.

Combine all fruit ingredients and place all in a large serving bowl. Pour mixture over fruit, tossing gently to coat. Cover and chill up to 24 hours.

Servings: 6

Target source of Vitamin C, Vitamin K, Manganese, Potassium, Dietary Fiber

Supportive of Immune and Gut Health

NO-BAKE COCOA MACAROONS

1/3 cup local raw honey

1/3 cup Clarified Butter, page 203

1 1/2 tsps cocoa powder

1/3 cup almond butter

1 tsp pure vanilla extract

2 cups shredded unsweetened coconut flakes

Nutrition Facts		
Serving Size 2 each (18g)		
Servings Per Container 24		
Amount Per Serving		
Calories 120	Calories from Fat 90	
		% Daily Value*
Total Fat 10g		15%
Saturated Fat 6g		30%
Trans Fat 0g		
Cholesterol 10mg		3%
Sodium 10mg		0%
Total Carbohydrate 6g		2%
Dietary Fiber 1g		4%
Sugars 4g		
Protein 1g		
Vitamin A 2%	• Vitamin C 0%	
Calcium 2%	• Iron 2%	

*Percent Daily Values are based on a 2,000 calorie diet. Your daily values may be higher or lower depending on your calorie needs

	Calories	2,000	2,500
Total Fat	Less than	65g	80g
Saturated Fat	Less than	20g	25g
Cholesterol	Less than	300mg	300mg
Sodium	Less than	2,400mg	2,400mg
Total Carbohydrate		300g	375g
Dietary Fiber		25g	30g

Calories per gram:
Fat 9 • Carbohydrate 4 • Protein 4

Prepare Clarified Butter.

Combine honey and clarified butter with cocoa powder in a medium saucepan over medium heat. Bring mixture to a boil. Boil for 1 minute and immediately remove from heat.

Stir in almond butter and vanilla until incorporated. Stir in coconut flakes; mix becomes harder to stir. Scoop or spoon small balls onto wax paper or parchment paper and put in the refrigerator until set.

Store in the refrigerator until service.

Servings: 24

Target source of Dietary Fats

Honey is great for Immune Health

161.

ZUCCHINI CREPES, BACON FLAVORED

4 free-range eggs, beaten

1 tbsp coconut flour

1/8-1/4 tsp fine grain sea salt

1/8-1/4 tsp ground black pepper

2 1/4 cups grated zucchini, peeled

2-4 tbsps reserved bacon fat or Clarified Butter

Nutrition Facts

Serving Size 2 crepes (129g)
Servings Per Container 4

Amount Per Serving

Calories 150   Calories from Fat 100

	% Daily Value*
Total Fat 12g	18%
Saturated Fat 7g	35%
Trans Fat 0g	
Cholesterol 215mg	72%
Sodium 150mg	6%
Total Carbohydrate 4g	1%
Dietary Fiber 1g	4%
Sugars 3g	
Protein 7g	

Vitamin A 8%	•	Vitamin C 20%
Calcium 4%	•	Iron 6%

*Percent Daily Values are based on a 2,000 calorie diet. Your daily values may be higher or lower depending on your calorie needs.

		Calories	2,000	2,500
Total Fat	Less than		65g	80g
Saturated Fat	Less than		20g	25g
Cholesterol	Less than		300mg	300mg
Sodium	Less than		2,400mg	2,400mg
Total Carbohydrate			300g	375g
Dietary Fiber			25g	30g

Calories per gram:
Fat 9 • Carbohydrate 4 • Protein 4

Combine beaten eggs, coconut flour, sea salt and black pepper; whisk well until smooth and eggs are combined. Add zucchini; mix until well incorporated.

Heat reserved bacon fat or clarified butter in a skillet over medium-low heat. Once the oil is heated, spoon the mixture into the skillet in the shape of a round crepe; approximately 5- 6 inches wide. Cook until they hold together. Using a metal spatula, carefully turn over crepe and cook until done, but not rubbery.

Tips
If you do not have bacon or bacon fat reserved (4-6 slices), please sub out with clarified butter, page 203.

Clean clarified butter; still get the flavor, without all the bad.

Servings: 8 crepes

Target source of Protein, Dietary Fats, Vitamin C, Vitamin B12, Molybdenum

Supportive of Immune Health

BREAD

ALMOND BREAD (2 BATCHES)

4 1/4 cups almond flour

6 tbsps coconut flour

1 cup ground flax meal

1 tsp fine grain sea salt

4 tsps baking soda

14 free-range eggs

1/2 cup extra virgin olive oil

1/4 cup local raw honey

1/4 cup Mother's apple cider vinegar

2 tsps pure almond or vanilla extract

Nutrition Facts

Serving Size 1 muffin (2oz) (54g)
Servings Per Container 30

Amount Per Serving

Calories 190	Calories from Fat 130

	% Daily Value*
Total Fat 15g	**23%**
Saturated Fat 2g	**10%**
Trans Fat 0g	
Cholesterol 100mg	**33%**
Sodium 280mg	**12%**
Total Carbohydrate 8g	**3%**
Dietary Fiber 3g	**12%**
Sugars 3g	
Protein 7g	

Vitamin A 2%	•	Vitamin C 0%
Calcium 4%	•	Iron 6%

*Percent Daily Values are based on a 2,000 calorie diet. Your daily values may be higher or lower depending on your calorie needs.

	Calories	2,000	2,500
Total Fat	Less than	65g	80g
Saturated Fat	Less than	20g	25g
Cholesterol	Less than	300mg	300mg
Sodium	Less than	2,400mg	2,400mg
Total Carbohydrate		300g	375g
Dietary Fiber		25g	30g

Calories per gram:
Fat 9 • Carbohydrate 4 • Protein 4

Preheat oven to 350°F.

Place almond flour, coconut flour, flax meal, sea salt and baking soda in a food processor; pulse and mix thoroughly. Alternatively, you can mix by hand or by hand blender.

Pulse in the eggs, oil, honey and vinegar; mix thoroughly. Add 1 1/4 cup of any dried fruit at this point; pulse, optional.

Pour batter into 2 greased 7.5" x 3.5" (or 8.5" x 4.5") sprayed or lined loaf pan, evenly. Or fill a mini-muffin pan sprayed with cooking spray. Bake for 25-30 minutes until center is cooked through. Test with a toothpick. Cool and serve.

Tips
Add local raw honey for a sweet delectable taste.

I prefer to make 2 batches at a time to freeze for later.

Crumble for recipes calling for bread crumbs or panko.

Yield: 2 loaves or up to 30 muffins

Target source of Magnesium, Dietary Fats, Dietary Fiber, Protein, Vitamin B12

Supportive of Immune Health

168.

NO NUT BANANA BREAD

1/2 cup coconut flour

1/2 tsp baking soda

1/4 tsp cream of tartar

2 tbsps arrowroot

1/4 tsp fine grain sea salt

1 tbsp ground cinnamon

4 mashed ripe banana

1/4 cup melted Clarified Butter, page 203

6 free-range eggs

1 tbsp pure vanilla extract

3 tbsps maple syrup, grade B

Nutrition Facts	
Serving Size 3 oz slice (85g)	
Servings Per Container 12	
Amount Per Serving	
Calories 160	Calories from Fat 70
	% Daily Value*
Total Fat 8g	12%
Saturated Fat 4g	20%
Trans Fat 0g	
Cholesterol 120mg	40%
Sodium 140mg	6%
Total Carbohydrate 18g	6%
Dietary Fiber 3g	12%
Sugars 10g	
Protein 4g	
Vitamin A 8% • Vitamin C 6%	
Calcium 2% • Iron 4%	

*Percent Daily Values are based on a 2,000 calorie diet. Your daily values may be higher or lower depending on your calorie needs.

	Calories	2,000	2,500
Total Fat	Less than	65g	80g
Saturated Fat	Less than	20g	25g
Cholesterol	Less than	300mg	300mg
Sodium	Less than	2,400mg	2,400mg
Total Carbohydrate		300g	375g
Dietary Fiber		25g	30g

Calories per gram
Fat 9 • Carbohydrate 4 • Protein 4

Preheat oven to 350°.

Prepare Clarified Butter.

Dry Ingredients: combine coconut flour, baking soda, cream of tartar, arrowroot, sea salt and ground cinnamon; mix well and set aside. *Wet Ingredient:* whisk eggs until frothy. Add banana, clarified butter, vanilla extract and maple syrup.

Add dry ingredients to wet ingredients; mix well.

Pour batter into a greased 7.5" x 3.5" (or 8.5" x 4.5") sprayed or lined loaf pan. Alternatively, I fill a mini-muffin pan sprayed with cooking spray. Bake 50-60 minutes until toothpick comes out clean.

Yield: 12 slices

Target source of Protein, Dietary Fiber, Dietary Fats, Vitamin A, Vitamin B12, Manganese, Potassium

Supportive of Immune and Gut Health

169.

PIZZA

ACAPULCO CHICKEN PIZZA

2 cups free-range boneless, skinless chicken, cut into
   1-inch cubes

2 tbsps extra virgin olive oil

2 tbsps Taco Seasoning, page 221

1 tbsp organic cayenne

1 cup shredded organic romaine lettuce
   (or spinach, kale, bok choy)

3/4 cup freshly diced pineapple

2/3 cup diced organic tomato

2 large diced avocado

1 freshly squeezed lemon juice, to prevent browning

1 cup Pizza Sauce, page 250

1 Pizza Crust, page 174

Nutrition Facts

Serving Size 1 slice (230g)
Servings Per Container 8

Amount Per Serving

Calories 400	Calories from Fat 230

	% Daily Value*
Total Fat 26g	40%
Saturated Fat 3.5g	18%
Trans Fat 0g	
Cholesterol 50mg	17%
Sodium 2010mg	84%
Total Carbohydrate 36g	12%
Dietary Fiber 4g	16%
Sugars 4g	
Protein 14g	

Vitamin A 30%	•	Vitamin C 35%
Calcium 6%	•	Iron 15%

*Percent Daily Values are based on a 2,000 calorie diet. Your daily values may be higher or lower depending on your calorie needs.

	Calories	2,000	2,500
Total Fat	Less than	65g	80g
Saturated Fat	Less than	20g	25g
Cholesterol	Less than	300mg	300mg
Sodium	Less than	2,400mg	2,400mg
Total Carbohydrate		300g	375g
Dietary Fiber		25g	30g

Calories per gram
Fat 9 • Carbohydrate 4 • Protein 4

Preheat oven to 400° F.

Prepare Taco Seasoning, Pizza Sauce and Pizza Crust.

Heat the oil in a large skillet over medium-high heat. Add chicken, taco seasoning and cayenne; sauté until cooked through and chicken begins to brown on the edges, about 10-15 minutes; stirring occasionally. Internal temperature should read 165° F, at the thickest part. Add 1/2 cup basic tomato sauce. Remove from heat; mix well.

Place crust on a sheet pan sprayed with cooking oil, spread the remaining 1/2 cup pizza sauce over crust and sprinkle chicken, romaine lettuce, pineapple and tomato over the top. Bake 7-10 minutes to heat through. Remove from the oven and garnish with avocado.

Servings: 8

Target source of Protein, Dietary Fiber, Dietary Fats, Vitamin A, Vitamin C, Vitamin K, Iron, Manganese, Potassium

Supportive of Immune Health

ALMOND PIZZA CRUST

2 cups almond meal

2 free-range eggs

3 tbsps extra virgin olive oil

1/4 tsp baking soda

1/2 tbsp Mother's apple cider vinegar

1 tsp garlic powder

1 1/2 tbsps chopped fresh rosemary or 1 1/2 tsps dried
   rosemary

Nutrition Facts

Serving Size 2 slices (95g)
Servings Per Container 4

Amount Per Serving

Calories 450   Calories from Fat 360

% Daily Value*

Total Fat 41g	63%
Saturated Fat 4g	20%
Trans Fat 0g	
Cholesterol 110mg	37%
Sodium 130mg	5%
Total Carbohydrate 13g	4%
Dietary Fiber 6g	24%
Sugars 3g	
Protein 15g	

Vitamin A 4%	Vitamin C 0%
Calcium 15%	Iron 15%

*Percent Daily Values are based on a 2,000 calorie diet. Your daily values may be higher or lower depending on your calorie needs.

		Calories:	2,000	2,500
Total Fat	Less than		65g	80g
Saturated Fat	Less than		20g	25g
Cholesterol	Less than		300mg	300mg
Sodium	Less than		2,400mg	2,400mg
Total Carbohydrate			300g	375g
Dietary Fiber			25g	30g

Calories per gram:
Fat 9 • Carbohydrate 4 • Protein 4

Preheat your oven to 350° F.

Combine all the ingredients into a mixing bowl; mix well to incorporate. Dough should be thick and a little sticky.

Form the dough into a ball and place on a lightly greased pizza pan or sheet pan with oil. Place the ball of the dough in the center of your pan and press in the center and out to expand dough. Pinch together any breaks and lightly push from center out until you have desired shape and thickness. If it is too thick, make two pizzas or just take that portion out and freeze for a small quick pizza later. It's roughly 12 inches across.

Bake the crust for 20 minutes. Prepare toppings while your dough is cooking. Turn up the oven heat to 400° F.

Add sauce and toppings and bake for an additional 15-20 minutes. Edges will begin to brown; remove from the oven and let cool slightly.

Tips
For EGG Replacement, use flax egg, page 204, OR replace egg with 2-4 tablespoons, which will also add moisture.

You want a dough consistency. It will be a little stickier. Use oil on your fingertips to avoid it sticking to your fingertips.

Add Fiber to your crust by replacing 1/2 the amount of almond meal, with flax meal.

Yield: 9" pizza round

Target source of Protein, Dietary Fiber, Dietary Fats, Iron, Calcium, Magnesium

BLUEBERRY TORTILLA PIZZA

1 cup fresh blueberry

1 cup sliced organic strawberry

2 tbsps coconut sugar

2 tsps cinnamon

2 tbsps melted Clarified Butter, page 203

1/2 cup coconut milk, full fat

1/2 cup toasted unsweetened shredded coconut

2 batches Tortilla Base, page 198

Nutrition Facts

Serving Size 1 slice (181g)
Servings Per Container 5

Amount Per Serving

Calories 300   Calories from Fat 210

	% Daily Value*
Total Fat 23g	35%
Saturated Fat 14g	70%
Trans Fat 0g	
Cholesterol 190mg	63%
Sodium 1250mg	52%
Total Carbohydrate 19g	6%
Dietary Fiber 6g	24%
Sugars 11g	
Protein 8g	

Vitamin A 10%	•	Vitamin C 40%
Calcium 6%	•	Iron 15%

*Percent Daily Values are based on a 2,000 calorie diet. Your daily values may be higher or lower depending on your calorie needs.

	Calories	2,000	2,500
Total Fat	Less than	65g	80g
Saturated Fat	Less than	20g	25g
Cholesterol	Less than	300mg	300mg
Sodium	Less than	2,400mg	2,400mg
Total Carbohydrate		300g	375g
Dietary Fiber		25g	30g

Calories per gram
Fat 9 • Carbohydrate 4 • Protein 4

Preheat broiler.

Prepare Clarified Butter and Tortilla Base recipe.

Refrigerate coconut milk can upside down for 30 minute, to separate coconut fat from the coconut juice. Combine coconut sugar and cinnamon. In a small bowl, combine blueberry and strawberry.

Lay tortillas on a sheet pan sprayed with cooking oil. Lightly brush tortillas with clarified butter and sprinkle with cinnamon sugar. Broil about 4-inches from the heat source, until lightly browned, about 3 minutes.

Cool slightly. Spread a light layer of chilled coconut milk, full fat on top of tortilla. Do not add coconut milk too early, or it will melt; keep chilled until ready to layer. Add fruit mixture and sprinkle with toasted unsweetened coconut.

Tip

Refrigerate full fat coconut milk can upside down for 30 minutes or longer. I always store mine in the refrigerator.

Servings: 10 Tortillas

Target source of Protein, Dietary Fiber, Dietary Fats, Vitamin C, Iron, Manganese

Supportive of Immune Health

CHICAGO-STYLE PIZZA

1 lb grass-fed ground beef or 93/7 lean ground beef

1/2 cup sliced fresh mushroom

1/2 cup chopped onion

1/2 cup chopped organic green bell pepper

1/2 cup chopped organic red bell pepper

1 tbsp chopped fresh basil or 1 tsp dried basil

1/4 tsp chopped fresh oregano or 1 tsp dried oregano

1/8 tsp crushed fennel seed

1/4 tsp fine grain sea salt

1 cup Pizza Sauce, page 250

1 Pizza Crust, page 174

Nutrition Facts		
Serving Size 1 slice (178g)		
Servings Per Container 8		
Amount Per Serving		
Calories 370	Calories from Fat 230	
		% Daily Value*
Total Fat 26g		40%
Saturated Fat 7g		35%
Trans Fat 0.5g		
Cholesterol 65mg		22%
Sodium 460mg		19%
Total Carbohydrate 28g		9%
Dietary Fiber 1g		4%
Sugars 2g		
Protein 12g		
Vitamin A 10%	•	Vitamin C 40%
Calcium 4%	•	Iron 10%

*Percent Daily Values are based on a 2,000 calorie diet. Your daily values may be higher or lower depending on your calorie needs.

		Calories:	2,000	2,500
Total Fat	Less than		65g	80g
Saturated Fat	Less than		20g	25g
Cholesterol	Less than		300mg	300mg
Sodium	Less than		2,400mg	2,400mg
Total Carbohydrate			320g	375g
Dietary Fiber			25g	30g

Calories per gram
Fat 9 • Carbohydrate 4 • Protein 4

Preheat oven to 400° F.

Prepare Pizza Crust and Pizza Sauce.

Heat a skillet over medium-high heat. Add beef, mushroom, onion, bell peppers, basil, oregano, crushed fennel and sea salt; sauté until meat is browned, about 7-10 minutes, no pink. Remove skillet from the stove and strain beef juices; place in a mixing bowl.

Spread 1 cup of pizza sauce over crust and sprinkle mixture over top. Bake for 20 minutes on bottom rack. Remove from the oven and let cool.

Servings: 8

Target source of Protein, Dietary Fats, Iron, Vitamin C, Vitamin A, Vitamin K

EGGPLANT PIZZA, NO CRUST

2 eggplant, peeled and cut into 1-inch slices

4 tbsps extra virgin olive oil

2 cups Pizza Sauce, page 250

Nutrition Facts

Serving Size 3-4 each (263g)
Servings Per Container 4

Amount Per Serving

Calories 120   Calories from Fat 50

	% Daily Value*
Total Fat 6g	9%
Saturated Fat 1g	5%
Trans Fat 0g	
Cholesterol 0mg	0%
Sodium 100mg	4%
Total Carbohydrate 17g	6%
Dietary Fiber 6g	24%
Sugars 8g	
Protein 3g	

Vitamin A 6%	•	Vitamin C 20%	
Calcium 4%	•	Iron 6%	

*Percent Daily Values are based on a 2,000 calorie diet. Your daily values may be higher or lower depending on your calorie needs.

	Calories	2,000	2,500
Total Fat	Less than	65g	80g
Saturated Fat	Less than	20g	25g
Cholesterol	Less than	300mg	300mg
Sodium	Less than	2,400mg	2,400mg
Total Carbohydrate		300g	375g
Dietary Fiber		25g	30g

Calories per gram

Fat 9 • Carbohydrate 4 • Protein 4

TOPPING OPTIONS

Grass-fed ground hamburger or 93/7 lean ground beef

Canadian bacon, pineapple and vegetables

Supreme toppings (red onion, black olive, tomato, uncured
   pepperoni, canadian bacon, vegetables)

NO Cheese

Preheat the oven or toaster oven to 425° F.

Prepare Pizza Sauce.

Slice eggplant and brush both sides of the eggplant with the oil; season with salt and pepper. Arrange eggplant circles on a sheet pan sprayed with cooking oil. Spread 2-4 tablespoons of pizza sauce on each eggplant slice. Top with vegetables, meats or other pizza toppings.

Bake for 8-12 minutes or until browned and almost tender, and heated throughout.

Servings: 4

Target source of Dietary Fiber, Vitamin C, Manganese, Molybdenum, Potassium

Supportive of Immune Health

FRUIT-E-RONI PIZZA

2 thinly sliced organic peach, cored

2 thinly sliced organic plums with skin, cored

6 oz uncured sliced pepperoni

1 cup Pizza Sauce, page 250

1 Pizza Crust, page 174

Nutrition Facts
Serving Size 1 slice (164g)
Servings Per Container 8

Amount Per Serving

Calories 360   Calories from Fat 230

% Daily Value*

Total Fat 26g — 40%

Saturated Fat 6g — 30%

Trans Fat 0g

Cholesterol 45mg — 15%

Sodium 750mg — 31%

Total Carbohydrate 31g — 10%

Dietary Fiber 2g — 8%

Sugars 6g

Protein 6g

Vitamin A 8% • Vitamin C 15%

Calcium 2% • Iron 6%

*Percent Daily Values are based on a 2,000 calorie diet. Your daily values may be higher or lower depending on your calorie needs.

	Calories	2,000	2,500
Total Fat	Less than	65g	80g
Saturated Fat	Less than	20g	25g
Cholesterol	Less than	300mg	300mg
Sodium	Less than	2,400mg	2,400mg
Total Carbohydrate		300g	375g
Dietary Fiber		25g	30g

Calories per gram:
Fat 9 • Carbohydrate 4 • Protein 4

Preheat oven to 425° F.

Prepare Pizza Sauce and Pizza Crust.

Spread the pizza sauce onto crust. Add fruit and pepperoni; bake for 15 minutes until heated through.

Tip
Pizza crust and sauce can be made ahead of time; great recipe to freeze.

Servings: 8

Target source of Dietary Fats, Dietary Fiber, Vitamin C, Vitamin K

Supportive of Immune Health

GREEK INSPIRED SAUSAGE

1 1/2 cups uncured sliced Italian sausage

2 tbsps extra virgin olive oil

1/2 cup organic chopped olive

3 tbsps chopped organic sun-dried tomato

1 cup organic chopped artichoke heart

1 tbsp Greek Seasoning, page 212

1 cup Pizza Sauce, page 250

1 Pizza Crust, page 174

Preheat oven to 400° F.

Prepare Greek Seasoning, Pizza Sauce and Pizza Crust.

Cook sausage on the grill or bake in the oven at 400° F, for about 10-15 minutes, until sizzling and heated through. Remove from the oven and let cool slightly. Slice sausage.

Heat the oil in the skillet over medium heat. Add olive, sun-dried tomato and artichoke heart; stir occasionally until softened. Add sausage and sauté for 3-5 minutes to infuse flavors.

Spread pizza sauce onto crust; sprinkle sausage mixture over the top. Bake for 10-15 minutes until heated through.

Servings: 4

Target source of Dietary Fats, Vitamin C, Vitamin K, Iron, Calcium

JERK CHICKEN, PINEAPPLE & CANADIAN BACON PIZZA

2 free-range, pastured chicken breasts or thighs, cut into
        1-inch cubes

1 1/2 tbsps Jamaican Jerk Seasoning, page 214

1 tbsp freshly squeezed lemon juice

1/2 tsp fine grain sea salt, to taste

1/2 tsp ground black pepper to, taste

1/3 cup finely diced uncured Canadian bacon

1/3 cup freshly chopped pineapple

1 cup Pizza Sauce, page 250

1 Pizza Crust, page 174

Preheat oven to 400° F.

Prepare Pizza Sauce, Pizza Crust and Jamaican Jerk Seasoning.

Wash and pat chicken dry with a paper towel. Cut raw chicken into 1-inch cubes. Sprinkle both sides with Jamaican jerk seasoning, lemon juice, sea salt and black pepper. Marinade in the refrigerator for 30 minutes, up to overnight.

Heat the oil in a grill pan over medium-high heat. Add chicken; grill for 12-15 minutes. Chicken will be mostly done; set aside. Spread the pizza sauce over the crust. Sprinkle chicken, Canadian bacon and pineapple. Bake for 15-20 minutes until heated through. Internal temperature of chicken should read 165° F, at the thickest part.

Tip
Sanitation: when handling raw foods, be sure to clean your hands and sanitize utensils well.

Servings: 4

Target source of Protein, Dietary Fats, Vitamin C, Vitamin K, B Vitamins

Supportive of Immune Health

PIZZA CRUST, FLAT BREAD & CRACKER DOUGH

1 1/2 cups tapioca flour

1/2 cup extra virgin olive oil

1 free-range egg

1/2 cup water

2 tbsps almond flour

1 tbsp crushed fresh garlic clove or 1 tsp garlic powder

1 tsp Italian Seasoning, page 213

1 tsp fine grain sea salt

Preheat oven to 350° F.

Prepare Italian Seasoning.

Nutrition Facts		
Serving Size 1 flat bread (122g)		
Servings Per Container 4		
Amount Per Serving		
Calories 420	Calories from Fat 270	
		% Daily Value*
Total Fat 31g		48%
Saturated Fat 4.5g		23%
Trans Fat 0g		
Cholesterol 55mg		18%
Sodium 600mg		25%
Total Carbohydrate 47g		16%
Dietary Fiber 1g		4%
Sugars 1g		
Protein 3g		
Vitamin A 2%	•	Vitamin C 0%
Calcium 4%	•	Iron 6%

*Percent Daily Values are based on a 2,000 calorie diet. Your daily values may be higher or lower depending on your calorie needs.

	Calories	2,000	2,500
Total Fat	Less than	65g	80g
Saturated Fat	Less than	20g	25g
Cholesterol	Less than	300mg	300mg
Sodium	Less than	2,400mg	2,400mg
Total Carbohydrate		300g	375g
Dietary Fiber		25g	30g

Calories per gram
Fat 9 • Carbohydrate 4 • Protein 4

Combine tapioca flour and oil together in mixing bowl. Stir with a spoon, and then mix together with your hands. The dough should be fully combined and choppy. Place tapioca mixture in a skillet over medium-low to medium heat; sauté until tapioca begins to start browning a little, about 7-minutes. Remove from stove and slightly cool to room temperature. Cooling to room temperature is a very important step.

Beat egg and water together. Add almond flour, garlic, Italian seasoning and sea salt to egg mixture; mix well. Add almond flour mixture with cooled tapioca. Mix well with your hands to combine and fully incorporate.

On a sheet pan sprayed with cooking oil, mash down dough to thin crust; filling in any gaps that break. Bake for 25 minutes until slightly dry and lightly yellow-brown.

Servings: 4

Target source of Protein, Dietary Fats, Vitamin K

Supportive of Immune Health

PORTOBELLO MUSHROOM AND PEPPER PIZZA

1 cup fresh Portobello mushroom, cut into strips
  OR 2 cups sliced baby Portobello
1 cup organic red bell pepper, seed and rib removed, cut into
  strips and into half
3 tbsps organic Italian salad dressing
2 tbsps chopped fresh parsley or 2 tsps dried parsley
1 cup Pizza Sauce, page 250
1 Pizza Crust, page 174

Nutrition Facts

Serving Size 1 slice (137g)
Servings Per Container 8

Amount Per Serving

Calories 260   Calories from Fat 160

% Daily Value*

Total Fat 18g — 28%
  Saturated Fat 2.5g — 13%
  Trans Fat 0g
Cholesterol 25mg — 8%
Sodium 400mg — 17%
Total Carbohydrate 29g — 10%
  Dietary Fiber 2g — 8%
  Sugars 3g
Protein 3g

Vitamin A 15% • Vitamin C 35%
Calcium 2% • Iron 6%

*Percent Daily Values are based on a 2,000 calorie diet. Your daily values may be higher or lower depending on your calorie needs.

	Calories	2,000	2,500
Total Fat	Less than	65g	80g
Saturated Fat	Less than	20g	25g
Cholesterol	Less than	300mg	300mg
Sodium	Less than	2,400mg	2,400mg
Total Carbohydrate		300g	375g
Dietary Fiber		25g	30g

Calories per gram
Fat 9 • Carbohydrate 4 • Protein 4

Preheat oven to 450° F.

Prepare Pizza Sauce and Pizza Crust.

Cut the mushroom and bell pepper into thin slices; about 2 cups. In a large bowl, combine mushroom, bell pepper and dressing; mix well. Spread pizza sauce onto crust; add mushroom and bell pepper.

Bake until mushrooms are tender, about 10-12 minutes. Garnish with parsley.

Tip
Variation: Replace mushroom and bell pepper with 1/2 cup thinly sliced plum tomato, green onion or pepperoni.

Servings: 4

Target source of Dietary Fats, Vitamin C, Vitamin K

Supportive of Immune Health

SQUARE TURKEY PIZZA

1 lb free-range pastured ground turkey

1/2 cup finely chopped shallot

1/8 tsp fine grain sea salt

1/8 tsp ground black pepper

1/2 tsp Italian Seasoning, page 213

1 cup Pizza Sauce, page 250

1 Pizza Crust, pressed thin, page 174

Preheat oven to 400° F.

Prepare Italian Seasoning, Pizza Sauce and Pizza Crust.

Heat a skillet over medium-high heat. Add turkey and shallot; sauté for 4 to 5 minutes; no pink. Add Italian seasoning, sea salt, black pepper and pizza sauce; simmer 5 minutes until mixture thickens.

Press crust into a thin layer, 1/2-inch or less; cut into squares. Carefully remove squares and place on a sheet pan sprayed with cooking oil; bake for 15 minutes. Remove from the oven and set aside to cool slightly.

Spread turkey and pizza sauce mixture onto squares; bake 12-15 minutes until golden brown. Remove and cool on wire rack.

Servings: 4

Target source of Protein, Dietary Fats, Vitamin C, Vitamin K, Iron

Supportive of Immune Health

VEGGIE AND EGG PIZZA

1 cup fresh chopped organic spinach leaves

2 cups broccoli florets, with stem

3/4 cup thinly sliced organic yellow squash

1/2 cup finely chopped red onion

1/ 2 tsp fine grain sea salt

1/2 tsp ground black pepper

2 tbsps extra virgin olive oil

2 free-range eggs

1 tbsp finely chopped fresh basil or 1 tsp dried basil

1/2 tbsp finely chopped fresh rosemary or 1/2 tsp dried
    rosemary

1 tsp minced garlic clove

1 cup Pizza Sauce, page 250

1 Pizza Crust, page 174

Nutrition Facts

Serving Size 1 slice (161g)
Servings Per Container 8

Amount Per Serving

Calories 290	Calories from Fat 180

	% Daily Value*
Total Fat 21g	**32%**
Saturated Fat 3g	**15%**
Trans Fat 0g	
Cholesterol 80mg	**27%**
Sodium 520mg	**22%**
Total Carbohydrate 29g	**10%**
Dietary Fiber 2g	**8%**
Sugars 2g	
Protein 4g	

Vitamin A 25%	•	Vitamin C 45%
Calcium 6%	•	Iron 8%

*Percent Daily Values are based on a 2,000 calorie diet. Your daily values may be higher or lower depending on your calorie needs.

	Calories	2,000	2,500
Total Fat	Less than	65g	80g
Saturated Fat	Less than	20g	25g
Cholesterol	Less than	300mg	300mg
Sodium	Less than	2,400mg	2,400mg
Total Carbohydrate		300g	375g
Dietary Fiber		25g	30g

Calories per gram
Fat 9 • Carbohydrate 4 • Protein 4

Preheat oven to 400° F.

Prepare Pizza Sauce and Pizza Crust.

Heat the oil in a skillet over medium-high heat. Add spinach, broccoli, squash and red onion; sauté for 5 minutes until crisp tender. Sprinkle with sea salt and black pepper; stir occasionally. Add the eggs, basil, rosemary and garlic clove; sauté until egg is cooked through, about 2-3 minutes, stirring often. Remove the skillet from the heat.

Spread pizza sauce over crust. Sprinkle vegetable and egg mixture over top; bake for 15-20 minutes until heated through and edges begin to brown.

Servings: 4

Target source of Dietary Fats, Vitamin A, Vitamin C, Vitamin K

Supportive of Immune Health

TORTILLAS

CHIPOTLE-LIME TORTILLAS

2 tbsps finely chopped organic chipottle adobo

2 tsps organic adobo sauce (in can with adobo chilies)

2 tbsps freshly squeezed lime juice

1 tsp minced garlic clove

1/8 cup finely chopped onion

1 pinch fine grain sea salt

2 Tortilla Base, page 198

Nutrition Facts
Serving Size 2 oz (56g)
Servings Per Container 5

Amount Per Serving

Calories 60	Calories from Fat 30

% Daily Value*

Total Fat 3.5g	5%
Saturated Fat 0g	0%
Trans Fat 0g	
Cholesterol 85mg	28%
Sodium 360mg	15%
Total Carbohydrate 3g	1%
Dietary Fiber 1g	4%
Sugars 1g	
Protein 3g	

Vitamin A 2%	•	Vitamin C 8%
Calcium 2%	•	Iron 4%

*Percent Daily Values are based on a 2,000 calorie diet. Your daily values may be higher or lower depending on your calorie needs.

	Calories:	2,000	2,500
Total Fat	Less than	65g	80g
Saturated Fat	Less than	20g	25g
Cholesterol	Less than	300mg	300mg
Sodium	Less than	2,400mg	2,400mg
Total Carbohydrate		300g	375g
Dietary Fiber		25g	30g

Calories per gram:
Fat 9 • Carbohydrate 4 • Protein 4

Preheat oven to 350° F.

Prepare Tortilla Base.

In a food processor, combine Chipotle adobo and sauce with lime, garlic, onion and sea salt; blend until smooth. Then add tortilla base recipe. Add chipotle mixture to flavor. ***Cooking instructions are provided on Tortilla Base, page198.***

Servings: 10 Tortillas

Target source of Vitamin B12

CHIPS

4 batches Tortilla Base + any flavor

Make your choice of flavored tortillas, then cut in four and bake at 350° F until crisp, about 5-7 minutes.

Servings: 4

Target source of Protein, Dietary Fats, Vitamin B12, Iron, Calcium, Potassium

192.

SPINACH AND KALE TORTILLAS

1/8 cup freshly chopped organic spinach

1/8 cup freshly chopped organic kale

1/4 each wedged sweet onion

1/2 minced garlic clove

1/2 tsp fine grain sea salt

1 Tortilla Base, page 198

Nutrition Facts

Serving Size 2 oz (57g)
Servings Per Container 5

Amount Per Serving	
Calories 50	Calories from Fat 30

	% Daily Value*
Total Fat 3g	5%
Saturated Fat 0g	0%
Trans Fat 0g	
Cholesterol 85mg	28%
Sodium 850mg	35%
Total Carbohydrate 3g	1%
Dietary Fiber 1g	4%
Sugars 1g	
Protein 4g	

Vitamin A 4%	•	Vitamin C 2%	
Calcium 2%	•	Iron 4%	

*Percent Daily Values are based on a 2,000 calorie diet. Your daily values may be higher or lower depending on your calorie needs.

	Calories	2,000	2,500
Total Fat	Less than	65g	80g
Saturated Fat	Less than	20g	25g
Cholesterol	Less than	300mg	300mg
Sodium	Less than	2,400mg	2,400mg
Total Carbohydrate		300g	375g
Dietary Fiber		25g	30g

Calories per gram:
Fat 9 • Carbohydrate 4 • Protein 4

Preheat oven to 350° F.

Prepare Tortilla Base.

Place spinach, kale, onion, garlic and sea salt in to blender and pulse to chop. Add to tortilla base; blend well. *Cooking instructions are provided on Tortilla Base, page 198.*

Servings: 5 Tortillas

Target source of Vitamin A, Vitamin K, Vitamin B12

Supportive of Detoxification Health

SUN-DRIED TOMATO BASIL TORTILLAS

3 tbsps organic sun-dried tomato

2 cups water

2 tbsps basil

2 tsps onion powder

2 tsps minced garlic clove

1/8 tsp fine grain sea salt

1 Tortilla Base, page 198

Nutrition Facts

Serving Size 1/2 oz (10g)
Servings Per Container 4

Amount Per Serving

Calories 25	Calories from Fat 0

	% Daily Value*
Total Fat 0g	0%
Saturated Fat 0g	0%
Trans Fat 0g	
Cholesterol 0mg	0%
Sodium 80mg	3%
Total Carbohydrate 4g	1%
Dietary Fiber 1g	4%
Sugars 2g	
Protein 1g	

Vitamin A 2%	•	Vitamin C 4%
Calcium 0%	•	Iron 2%

*Percent Daily Values are based on a 2,000 calorie diet. Your daily values may be higher or lower depending on your calorie needs.

	Calories:	2,000	2,500
Total Fat	Less than	65g	80g
Saturated Fat	Less than	20g	25g
Cholesterol	Less than	300mg	300mg
Sodium	Less than	2,400mg	2,400mg
Total Carbohydrate		300g	375g
Dietary Fiber		25g	30g

Calories per gram:
Fat 9 • Carbohydrate 4 • Protein 4

Preheat oven to 350° F.

Prepare Tortilla Base.

Steep the sun-dried tomato in water or vegetable stock in a small saucepan; bring to a boil. Remove saucepan from heat and soak for 15 minutes. Strain liquid.

Add sun-dried tomato, basil, onion powder, garlic and sea salt to the food processor and blend until smooth, with sun-dried tomato chopped smaller. *Cooking instructions are provided on Tortilla Base, page 198.*

Tip
For added flavor, soak sun-dried tomatoes in an organic stock or broth, instead of water.

Servings: 5 Tortillas

Target source of Vitamin C and Vitamin K

195.

196.

TOMATILLO TORTILLAS

1/2 cup organic tomatillo, seeded and roughly chopped

1/8 cup organic jalapeno pepper, seeded and roughly chopped

2 tsps minced garlic clove

2 tsps onion powder

1/4 tsp fine grain sea salt

1 Tortillas Base, page 198

Nutrition Facts

Serving Size 1 Tortilla (59g)
Servings Per Container 5

Amount Per Serving

Calories 60	Calories from Fat 30

	% Daily Value*
Total Fat 3.5g	5%
Saturated Fat 0g	0%
Trans Fat 0g	
Cholesterol 85mg	28%
Sodium 760mg	32%
Total Carbohydrate 4g	1%
Dietary Fiber 2g	8%
Sugars 1g	
Protein 4g	

Vitamin A 4%	•	Vitamin C 4%
Calcium 2%	•	Iron 4%

*Percent Daily Values are based on a 2,000 calorie diet. Your daily values may be higher or lower depending on your calorie needs.

	Calories	2,000	2,500
Total Fat	Less than	65g	80g
Saturated Fat	Less than	20g	25g
Cholesterol	Less than	300mg	300mg
Sodium	Less than	2,400mg	2,400mg
Total Carbohydrate		300g	375g
Dietary Fiber		25g	30g

Calories per gram:
Fat 9 • Carbohydrate 4 • Protein 4

Preheat oven to 350° F.

Prepare Tortilla Base.

Deseed and rinse tomatillo and jalapeno; rough chop. Bring water to boil in a saucepan. Add tomatillo and jalapeno and cook until soft, about 3-5 minutes.

In a food processor, blend tomatillo, jalapeno, onion powder, garlic and sea salt; blend until smooth. Add tortilla base; blend until smooth grainy pancake consistency. *Cooking instructions are provided on Tortilla Base, recipe pg 198.*

Servings: 5

Target source of Vitamin C

TORTILLA BASE

3 tbsps flaxseed meal or almond meal; split for combo

1/2 tsp baking soda

1/2 tsp cream of tartar

1 tsp fine grain sea salt

1/2 tsp crushed rosemary

2 free-range eggs, beaten

4 tbsps water, more if needed

Nutrition Facts	
Serving Size 1 oz (38g)	
Servings Per Container 5	
Amount Per Serving	
Calories 50	Calories from Fat 30
	% Daily Value*
Total Fat 3g	5%
Saturated Fat 0g	0%
Trans Fat 0g	
Cholesterol 85mg	28%
Sodium 620mg	26%
Total Carbohydrate 2g	1%
Dietary Fiber 1g	4%
Sugars 0g	
Protein 3g	
Vitamin A 2% • Vitamin C 0%	
Calcium 2% • Iron 4%	

*Percent Daily Values are based on a 2,000 calorie diet. Your daily values may be higher or lower depending on your calorie needs.

	Calories	2,000	2,500
Total Fat	Less than	65g	80g
Saturated Fat	Less than	20g	25g
Cholesterol	Less than	300mg	300mg
Sodium	Less than	2,400mg	2,400mg
Total Carbohydrate		300g	375g
Dietary Fiber		25g	30g

Calories per gram:
Fat 9 • Carbohydrate 4 • Protein 4

Preheat oven to 350° F.

In food processor or by hand, combine baking soda, cream of tartar and sea salt; mash well to break baking soda clumps. Add flaxseed or almond meal; mix well.

Beat egg and liquid together. Add wet ingredients to dry ingredients; mix well until batter is smooth grainy, pancake consistency. Let set for 5 minutes covered, to thicken. If batter becomes too thick, add 1 tablespoon of liquid at a time; mix well. Add liquid in small amounts, if too thick; mix well. You want pancake consistency.

Add flavored ingredients at this time.

Variations: Add additional herbs, 1 tablespoon at a time until you get to the flavor you like - onion powder, garlic powder, dried chive, sun-dried tomato, basil, spinach, etc.

Liberally spray a sheet pan with cooking spray. Add 3-4 tablespoons into circular shape until mixture is gone; up to five on pan. You want them thin with full coverage.

Place baking sheet pan in the oven for 7-10 minutes, until the middle of tortilla is cooked through; it should not be soggy in the center.

Using a metal spatula, carefully remove the edges and then throughto the center. Flip and cook for an additional 2 minutes. Leave in a tad longer until middle is cooked through.

Alternatively, you can place 3-4 tablespoons and spread on a plate, in shape of tortilla and place in microwave for 1:25 minutes.

Tips
You could add variation by replacing water with a flavored broth that is used in a recipe.

Make the tortillas any shape you need.

Servings: 5 tortillas

Target source of Vitamin B12 from eggs

FAT and OIL

BASIL OIL

4 tbsps extra virgin olive oil

2 tbsps finely minced fresh basil or 2 tsp dried

2 tbsps finely minced fresh parsley or 2 tsp dried

1/8 tsp fine sea salt

1/8 tsp ground black pepper

Nutrition Facts

Serving Size 2 Tbsp (35g)
Servings Per Container 2

Amount Per Serving

Calories 240	Calories from Fat 240

	% Daily Value*
Total Fat 28g	43%
Saturated Fat 4g	20%
Trans Fat 0g	
Cholesterol 0mg	0%
Sodium 150mg	6%
Total Carbohydrate 0g	0%
Dietary Fiber 0g	0%
Sugars 0g	
Protein 0g	

Vitamin A 10%	•	Vitamin C 10%
Calcium 2%	•	Iron 2%

*Percent Daily Values are based on a 2,000 calorie diet. Your daily values may be higher or lower depending on your calorie needs.

	Calories:	2,000	2,500
Total Fat	Less than	65g	80g
Saturated Fat	Less than	20g	25g
Cholesterol	Less than	300mg	300mg
Sodium	Less than	2,400mg	2,400mg
Total Carbohydrate		300g	375g
Dietary Fiber		25g	30g

Calories per gram
Fat 9 • Carbohydrate 4 • Protein 4

Combine the oil, basil, parsley, sea salt, and black pepper to a small bowl; stir well and add to any dish for extra flavoring.

Store in a dark airtight bottle.

Servings: 1/2 cup

Target source of Vitamin K, Vitamin C, Dietary Fats

CLARIFIED BUTTER

Use a minimum of 2 pounds of unsalted butter.

Heat a saucepan over medium-low heat. Add butter and gently stir with a wooden spoon; about 5 minutes. As the butter melts and begins to simmer, the milk protein solids will rise to the top. Slightly lower the temperature, if the butter begins to pop. You want gentle bubbles throughout. Allow the butter to simmer for 25-30 minutes until all milk rises to the top; time can vary.

Using a small fine mesh strainer, skim the milk solid off the top and discard. You will notice some milk solids at the bottom; leave them for now. Do not stir them up. Continue cooking for another 5-10 minutes until bottom layer of milk protein solids are beginning to brown. Watch carefully during the final 10 minutes to ensure you do not burn the butter. Continue skimming the top; butter should be clear when complete. Immediately remove butter from the stove top. Set aside to cool slightly.

Once cool, pour butter through a strainer lined with cheese cloth or a thick layer of folded paper towels will do; be sure to cover all mesh areas. You can store the butter any way you like but the muffin pan method has always been the best for me. I recommend dividing out into mini muffin pans, lightly sprayed with cooking spray for easy removal.

Use a measuring cup to pour into each space; creates less mess. Once they are all full, carefully place them in the freezer to harden.

The clarified butter can take up to 4 hours to solidify. Remove all mini butter piece and place in a zip lock storage bag and return to freezer. Each piece should measure about 1 1/2-2 ounces, or 3-4 tablespoons.

(Continued on the next page)

203.

Nutrition Facts

Serving Size 8g
Servings Per Container

Amount Per Serving

Calories 45	Calories From Fat 45

% Daily Value *

Total Fat 5g	8%
Saturated Fat 3g	16%
Trans Fat 0g	0%
Cholesterol 10mg	3%
Sodium 0mg	0%
Total Carbohydrates 0g	0%
Dietary Fiber 0g	0%
Soluble Fiber	
Sugars 0g	0%
Protein 0g	0%

Vitamin A	4%	Vitamin C	0%
Calcium	0%	Iron	0%
Thiamin	0%	Riboflavin	0%
Niacin	0%	Vitamin B6	0%
Phosphorus	0%	Zinc	0%

* Percent Daily values are based on a 2,000 calorie diet. Your daily value may be higher or lower depending on your calorie needs.

	Calories	2,000	2,500
Total Fat	Less than	65g	80g
Saturated Fat	Less than	20g	25g
Cholesterol	Less than	300mg	300mg
Sodium	Less than	2,400mg	2,400mg
Total Carbohydrate		300g	375g
Dietary Fiber		25g	30g

Our grandparents always use to leave their butter on the counter for days without refrigeration. Today we cannot do this because of the possibility of contaminated ingredients, in addition to sanitation issues with spoilage and bacteria. By removing the milk solids you will have less to worry about when leaving it on the counter to melt. You should always practice great food safety. *See Recipe Chef Notes, page 17*

Clarified Butter is a great option to use for cooking fat and an excellent substitution for grain butter in other recipes; making your dishes healthier.

Prepping ahead alleviates the need to grab the yucky butter when adding to a dish.

Tips

Grain-fed butter or regular butter is processed using grain-fed cow milk.

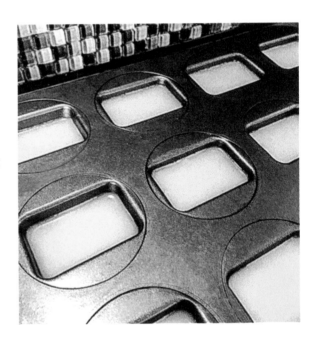

If you choose to eat dairy products, make a healthier choice by purchasing grass-fed butter (i.e. Kerigold Irish butter, cream cheese and other products can be found at health food stores nationwide).

Preparing clarified butter in advance allows you to have additional cooking fat options available, versus using only oils. You still get the butter flavor.

Clarified Butter is great for high temperature cooking, such as frying.

FLAX EGG (EGG REPLACEMENT)

1 tbsp flaxseed meal

2 1/2 tbsps water

Nutrition Facts
Serving Size 1 (44g)
Servings Per Container 1

Amount Per Serving

Calories 40	Calories from Fat 20

	% Daily Value*
Total Fat 2g	3%
Saturated Fat 0g	0%
Trans Fat 0g	
Cholesterol 0mg	0%
Sodium 0mg	0%
Total Carbohydrate 2g	1%
Dietary Fiber 2g	8%
Sugars 0g	
Protein 2g	

Vitamin A 0%	•	Vitamin C 0%
Calcium 2%	•	Iron 2%

*Percent Daily Values are based on a 2,000 calorie diet. Your daily values may be higher or lower depending on your calorie needs.

	Calories	2,000	2,500
Total Fat	Less than	65g	80g
Saturated Fat	Less than	20g	25g
Cholesterol	Less than	300mg	300mg
Sodium	Less than	2,400mg	2,400mg
Total Carbohydrate		300g	375g
Dietary Fiber		25g	30g

Calories per gram:
Fat 9 • Carbohydrate 4 • Protein 4

Add flaxseed meal and water to a bowl; mix well with a fork. Let rest for 5 minutes to thicken.

Tip
Flax Egg replaces one free-range egg in most recipes calling for egg. Flax egg does not bind well as an egg during some baking.

Serving: 1

Target source of Dietary Fiber, Unsaturated Fats, Calcium, Iron

Supportive of Estrogen Detoxification

SEASONINGS

ALLSPICE SEASONING

1 tbsp ground cinnamon

1 tbsp ground nutmeg

2 tsps minced garlic clove

2 tsps ground ginger

Nutrition Facts		
Serving Size 1.5 tsp (7g)		
Servings Per Container 4		
Amount Per Serving		
Calories 25	Calories from Fat 10	
		% Daily Value*
Total Fat 1g		2%
Saturated Fat 0g		0%
Trans Fat 0g		
Cholesterol 0mg		0%
Sodium 0mg		0%
Total Carbohydrate 4g		1%
Dietary Fiber 2g		8%
Sugars 0g		
Protein 0g		
Vitamin A 0%	•	Vitamin C 0%
Calcium 2%	•	Iron 2%

*Percent Daily Values are based on a 2,000 calorie diet. Your daily values may be higher or lower depending on your calorie needs.

		Calories:	2,000	2,800
Total Fat	Less than		65g	80g
Saturated Fat	Less than		20g	25g
Cholesterol	Less than		300mg	300mg
Sodium	Less than		2,400mg	2,400mg
Total Carbohydrate			300g	375g
Dietary Fiber			25g	30g

Calories per gram:
Fat 9 • Carbohydrate 4 • Protein 4

Mix all ingredients together, grind to an almost powder consistency and store in an airtight container for up to 6 months.

Yields: 1.5 ounces

ANYTHING SEASONING

1 tsp ground sage

1 tsp ground black pepper

1 tsp ground ginger

1 tsp ground coriander

1 tsp ground allspice

1 tsp onion powder

1 tsp dried minced garlic

1 tsp crushed dried thyme

1 tsp chopped dried rosemary

1 tsp chopped dried parsley

1 tsp crushed dried marjoram

1 tsp chopped dried oregano

Nutrition Facts	
Serving Size 4 tbsp (21g)	
Servings Per Container 1	
Amount Per Serving	
Calories 50	Calories from Fat 10
	% Daily Value*
Total Fat 1.5g	2%
Saturated Fat 0g	0%
Trans Fat 0g	
Cholesterol 0mg	0%
Sodium 15mg	1%
Total Carbohydrate 12g	4%
Dietary Fiber 5g	20%
Sugars 0g	
Protein 2g	
Vitamin A 4% • Vitamin C 6%	
Calcium 10% • Iron 20%	

*Percent Daily Values are based on a 2,000 calorie diet. Your daily values may be higher or lower depending on your calorie needs.

	Calories:	2,000	2,500
Total Fat	Less than	65g	80g
Saturated Fat	Less than	20g	25g
Cholesterol	Less than	300mg	300mg
Sodium	Less than	2,400mg	2,400mg
Total Carbohydrate		300g	375g
Dietary Fiber		25g	30g

Calories per gram:
Fat 9 • Carbohydrate 4 • Protein 4

Combine all dried herbs and spices; mix well, and store in an airtight container for up to 6 months. Add to ANY dish to compliment flavors.

Yields: 2.0 ounces

CURRY POWDER

1 tbsp of cardamom seeds

2 tsps ground coriander

2 tsps ground cumin

1 tsp ground turmeric

1/2 tsp ground organic chili powder

1/2 tsp ground black pepper

1/8 tsp ground fennel seed

Nutrition Facts

Serving Size 2 tbsp (17g)
Servings Per Container 1

Amount Per Serving

Calories 60	Calories from Fat 15

	% Daily Value*
Total Fat 2g	3%
Saturated Fat 0g	0%
Trans Fat 0g	
Cholesterol 0mg	0%
Sodium 50mg	2%
Total Carbohydrate 9g	3%
Dietary Fiber 5g	20%
Sugars 0g	
Protein 2g	

Vitamin A 0%	•	Vitamin C 2%
Calcium 8%	•	Iron 20%

*Percent Daily Values are based on a 2,000 calorie diet. Your daily values may be higher or lower depending on your calorie needs.

	Calories	2,000	2,500
Total Fat	Less than	65g	80g
Saturated Fat	Less than	20g	25g
Cholesterol	Less than	300mg	300mg
Sodium	Less than	2,400mg	2,400mg
Total Carbohydrate		300g	375g
Dietary Fiber		25g	30g

Calories per gram
Fat 9 • Carbohydrate 4 • Protein 4

In a spice grinder or with a mortar and pestle, combine all ingredients, grind to a powder and stor in an airtight container for up to 6 months.

Yield: 2 tablespoons

Supportive of Immune Health

FIVE SPICES SEASONING

4 tsp ground cinnamon

4 tsp ground clove

4 tsp ground star anise

4 tsp toasted ground fennel seed

4 tsp toasted ground black peppercorns

Nutrition Facts

Serving Size 8 tbsp (7g)
Servings Per Container 8

Amount Per Serving

Calories 15	Calories from Fat 5

	% Daily Value*
Total Fat 0.5g	1%
Saturated Fat 0g	0%
Trans Fat 0g	
Cholesterol 0mg	0%
Sodium 40mg	2%
Total Carbohydrate 3g	1%
Dietary Fiber 2g	8%
Sugars 0g	
Protein 1g	

Vitamin A 0%	•	Vitamin C 0%
Calcium 4%	•	Iron 6%

*Percent Daily Values are based on a 2,000 calorie diet. Your daily values may be higher or lower depending on your calorie needs:

		Calories	2,000	2,500
Total Fat	Less than		65g	80g
Saturated Fat	Less than		20g	25g
Cholesterol	Less than		300mg	300mg
Sodium	Less than		2,400mg	2,400mg
Total Carbohydrate			300g	375g
Dietary Fiber			25g	30g

Calories per gram:
Fat 9 • Carbohydrate 4 • Protein 4

Mix the spices together, grind and store in an airtight container.

Yield: 8 tablespoons

GREEK SEASONING

2 tbsps dried oregano

2 tbsps dried mint

2 tbsps dried thyme

1 tbsp dried basil

1 tbsp dried marjoram

1 tbsp minced dried onion

1/2 tbsp minced dried garlic

Nutrition Facts
Serving Size 2 Tbsp (7g)
Servings Per Container 4

Amount Per Serving

Calories 20 | Calories from Fat 5

% Daily Value*

Total Fat 0g — 0%
 Saturated Fat 0g — 0%
 Trans Fat 0g
Cholesterol 0mg — 0%
Sodium 5mg — 0%
Total Carbohydrate 5g — 2%
 Dietary Fiber 2g — 8%
 Sugars 1g
Protein 1g

Vitamin A 4% • Vitamin C 4%
Calcium 8% • Iron 20%

*Percent Daily Values are based on a 2,000 calorie diet. Your daily values may be higher or lower depending on your calorie needs.

| | Calories | 2,000 | 2,500 |
Total Fat | Less than | 65g | 80g
Saturated Fat | Less than | 20g | 25g
Cholesterol | Less than | 300mg | 300mg
Sodium | Less than | 2,400mg | 2,400mg
Total Carbohydrate | | 300g | 375g
 Dietary Fiber | | 25g | 30g

Calories per gram:
 Fat 9 • Carbohydrate 4 • Protein 4

Combine all ingredients together in a bowl; mix well, and store in an airtight container for up to 6 months.

Yield: 1/2 cup

ITALIAN SEASONING

3 tbsps dried basil

3 tbsps dried oregano

3 tbsps dried parsley

1 tbsp garlic powder

1 tsp onion powder

1 tsp dried thyme

1 tsp dried rosemary

1/4 tsp ground black pepper

1/4 tsp red pepper flakes

Nutrition Facts

Serving Size 1/2 tsp (3g)
Servings Per Container 11

Amount Per Serving

Calories 10	Calories from Fat 0

	% Daily Value*
Total Fat 0g	0%
Saturated Fat 0g	0%
Trans Fat 0g	
Cholesterol 0mg	0%
Sodium 0mg	0%
Total Carbohydrate 2g	1%
Dietary Fiber 1g	4%
Sugars 0g	
Protein 1g	

Vitamin A 2%	•	Vitamin C 2%
Calcium 4%	•	Iron 6%

*Percent Daily Values are based on a 2,000 calorie diet. Your daily values may be higher or lower depending on your calorie needs

	Calories	2,000	2,500
Total Fat	Less than	65g	80g
Saturated Fat	Less than	20g	25g
Cholesterol	Less than	300mg	300mg
Sodium	Less than	2,400mg	2,400mg
Total Carbohydrate		300g	375g
Dietary Fiber		25g	30g

Calories per gram:
Fat 9 • Carbohydrate 4 • Protein 4

Mix all ingredients in a spice grinder or with mortar and pestle; roughly ground, and store in an airtight container for up to 6 months.

Yield: 2/3 cup

213.

JAMAICAN JERK SEASONING

2 tsps finely chopped dried parsley

1 tsp ground allspice

1/4 tsp ground cinnamon

1 tsp ground black pepper

1/4 tsp ground cumin

1 tbsp garlic powder

2 tsps fine grain sea salt

1/4 tsp ground nutmeg

2 tsps ground dried chive

Nutrition Facts

Serving Size 1 1/2 tbsp (28g)
Servings Per Container 1

Amount Per Serving

Calories 50	Calories from Fat 5

% Daily Value*

Total Fat 0.5g	1%
Saturated Fat 0g	0%
Trans Fat 0g	
Cholesterol 0mg	0%
Sodium 4650mg	194%
Total Carbohydrate 11g	4%
Dietary Fiber 3g	12%
Sugars 0g	

Protein 2g

Vitamin A 2%	•	Vitamin C 6%
Calcium 6%	•	Iron 8%

*Percent Daily Values are based on a 2,000 calorie diet. Your daily values may be higher or lower depending on your calorie needs.

	Calories:	2,000	2,500
Total Fat	Less than	65g	80g
Saturated Fat	Less than	20g	25g
Cholesterol	Less than	300mg	300mg
Sodium	Less than	2,400mg	2,400mg
Total Carbohydrate		300g	375g
Dietary Fiber		25g	30g

Calories per gram:
Fat 9 • Carbohydrate 4 • Protein 4

Mix together all the ingredients and store in an airtight container for up to 6 months.

Tip
Use 1 1/2 tablespoon of seasoning for each pound of meat.

Yield: 1/3 cup

Target source of Vitamin K, Manganese, Vitamin B6

LEMON PEPPER SEASONING

4 tbsps zested lemon

1/3 cup crushed peppercorn, black or medley

1/4 cup iodized sea salt

Nutrition Facts

Serving Size 1 tbsp (15g)
Servings Per Container 12

Amount Per Serving

Calories 5	Calories from Fat 0

	% Daily Value*
Total Fat 0g	0%
Saturated Fat 0g	0%
Trans Fat 0g	
Cholesterol 0mg	0%
Sodium 2410mg	100%
Total Carbohydrate 1g	0%
Dietary Fiber 1g	4%
Sugars 0g	
Protein 0g	

Vitamin A 0%	•	Vitamin C 4%
Calcium 2%	•	Iron 0%

*Percent Daily Values are based on a 2,000 calorie diet. Your daily values may be higher or lower depending on your calorie needs.

	Calories	2,000	2,500
Total Fat	Less than	65g	80g
Saturated Fat	Less than	20g	25g
Cholesterol	Less than	300mg	300mg
Sodium	Less than	2,400mg	2,400mg
Total Carbohydrate		300g	375g
Dietary Fiber		25g	30g

Calories per gram:
Fat 9 • Carbohydrate 4 • Protein 4

Zest all the lemons and mix with crushed peppercorn. Spread out on sheet pan lined with parchment paper. Bake on the lowest setting until the lemon zest is dried entirely.

Add the lemon zest and the peppercorn to a grinder; grind to almost a powder. Mix with the iodized sea salt and store in an airtight container in the refrigerator for up to 1 month.

Yield: 2/3 cup

MONTREAL SEASONING

3 tsps fine grain sea salt

3 tsps ground black pepper

2 tsps onion powder

2 tsps garlic powder

1 tsp ground organic cayenne

1 tsp organic dried ground thyme

1 tsp organic dried rosemary

Nutrition Facts
Serving Size 1 tsp (3g)
Servings Per Container 12

Amount Per Serving

Calories 5 — Calories from Fat 0

% Daily Value*

Total Fat 0g	0%
Saturated Fat 0g	0%
Trans Fat 0g	
Cholesterol 0mg	0%
Sodium 390mg	16%
Total Carbohydrate 1g	0%
Dietary Fiber 0g	0%
Sugars 0g	
Protein 0g	

Vitamin A 2% • Vitamin C 0%
Calcium 0% • Iron 2%

*Percent Daily Values are based on a 2,000 calorie diet. Your daily values may be higher or lower depending on your calorie needs.

	Calories	2,000	2,500
Total Fat	Less than	65g	80g
Saturated Fat	Less than	20g	25g
Cholesterol	Less than	300mg	300mg
Sodium	Less than	2,400mg	2,400mg
Total Carbohydrate		300g	375g
Dietary Fiber		25g	30g

Calories per gram
Fat 9 • Carbohydrate 4 • Protein 4

Mix all ingredients together and mix well and store in an airtight container.

Servings: 5 tablespoons

POULTRY SEASONING

2 tsp ground dried sage

1 1/2 tsp ground dried thyme

1 tsp ground dried marjoram

3/4 tsp ground dried rosemary

1 tsp ground dried basil

1/2 tsp grated fresh nutmeg

1/2 tsp finely ground black pepper

Nutrition Facts

Serving Size 2 tsp (1.8g)
Servings Per Container 4

Amount Per Serving

Calories 5	Calories from Fat 0

	% Daily Value*
Total Fat 0g	0%
Saturated Fat 0g	0%
Trans Fat 0g	
Cholesterol 0mg	0%
Sodium 0mg	0%
Total Carbohydrate 1g	0%
Dietary Fiber 1g	4%
Sugars 0g	
Protein 0g	

Vitamin A 2%	•	Vitamin C 0%
Calcium 2%	•	Iron 4%

*Percent Daily Values are based on a 2,000 calorie diet. Your daily values may be higher or lower depending on your calorie needs.

	Calories	2,000	2,500
Total Fat	Less than	65g	80g
Saturated Fat	Less than	20g	25g
Cholesterol	Less than	300mg	300mg
Sodium	Less than	2,400mg	2,400mg
Total Carbohydrate		300g	375g
Dietary Fiber		25g	30g

Calories per gram
Fat 9 • Carbohydrate 4 • Protein 4

Combine sage, thyme, marjoram, rosemary, nutmeg, and black pepper; mix well and store in an airtight container.

Tip
Grate fresh nutmeg with a small Micro plane zester, or smaller cheese grater.

Yield: 2 1/2 tablespoons

217.

SAGE SEASONING

1/4 cup dried sage

3 tbsps dried marjoram

4 tbsps dried thyme

1 1/2 tsps organic celery seed

1/8 tsp fine grain sea salt

Nutrition Facts

Serving Size 1 tsp (5g)
Servings Per Container 6

Amount Per Serving

Calories 15	Calories from Fat 5

	% Daily Value*
Total Fat 0.5g	1%
Saturated Fat 0g	0%
Trans Fat 0g	
Cholesterol 0mg	0%
Sodium 55mg	2%
Total Carbohydrate 3g	1%
Dietary Fiber 2g	8%
Sugars 0g	
Protein 1g	

Vitamin A 4%	•	Vitamin C 4%
Calcium 8%	•	Iron 20%

*Percent Daily Values are based on a 2,000 calorie diet. Your daily values may be higher or lower depending on your calorie needs.

	Calories	2,000	2,500
Total Fat	Less than	65g	80g
Saturated Fat	Less than	20g	25g
Cholesterol	Less than	300mg	300mg
Sodium	Less than	2,400mg	2,400mg
Total Carbohydrate		300g	375g
Dietary Fiber		25g	30g

Calories per gram:
Fat 9 • Carbohydrate 4 • Protein 4

In a spice grinder, combine sage, marjoram, thyme, celery seeds and salt and pulse into a powder, and store in an airtight container.

Yield: 1/2 cup

SEASONING SALT

1/4 cup kosher salt

4 tsps ground black pepper

1 tsp ground paprika

1 tsp garlic powder

1/2 tsp onion powder

1/2 tsp ground red pepper flake

Nutrition Facts

Serving Size 1 tsp (4g)
Servings Per Container 18

Amount Per Serving

Calories 5	Calories from Fat 0

	% Daily Value*
Total Fat 0g	0%
Saturated Fat 0g	0%
Trans Fat 0g	
Cholesterol 0mg	0%
Sodium 1280mg	53%
Total Carbohydrate 1g	0%
Dietary Fiber 0g	0%
Sugars 0g	
Protein 0g	

Vitamin A 2%	•	Vitamin C 0%
Calcium 0%	•	Iron 0%

*Percent Daily Values are based on a 2,000 calorie diet. Your daily values may be higher or lower depending on your calorie needs.

	Calories	2,000	2,500
Total Fat	Less than	65g	80g
Saturated Fat	Less than	20g	25g
Cholesterol	Less than	300mg	300mg
Sodium	Less than	2,400mg	2,400mg
Total Carbohydrate		300g	375g
Dietary Fiber		25g	30g

Calories per gram:
Fat 9 • Carbohydrate 4 • Protein 4

Combine salt, black pepper, paprika, garlic powder, onion powder, and cayenne pepper in a mixing bowl; mix well and store in an airtight container.

Yield: 1/4 cup

STEAK SEASONING

2 tsps garlic powder

4 tsps crushed coriander seed

2 tbsps iodized salt

4 tsps chopped dill weed

2 tbsps minced onion

4 tsps ground paprika

4 tsps crushed red pepper flake

4 tsps fresh coarse peppercorn, black or medley

Mix together and store in an airtight container.

Yield: 1/4 cup

220.

TACO SEASONING

1/4 cup organic chili powder, plus 1 tbsp

1 1/4 tsps garlic powder

1 1/4 tsps onion powder

1 1/4 tsps crushed red pepper flake

1 1/4 tsps chopped dried oregano

2 1/2 tsps ground paprika

2 tbsps ground cumin, plus 1 1/2 tsps

1 tbsp fine grain sea salt, plus 2 tsps

1 tbsp ground black pepper, plus 2 tsps

Nutrition Facts		
Serving Size 2 tbsp (25g)		
Servings Per Container 4		
Amount Per Serving		
Calories 35	Calories from Fat 10	
		% Daily Value*
Total Fat 1g		2%
Saturated Fat 0g		0%
Trans Fat 0g		
Cholesterol 0mg		0%
Sodium 3210mg		134%
Total Carbohydrate 6g		2%
Dietary Fiber 3g		12%
Sugars 0g		
Protein 1g		
Vitamin A 15%	•	Vitamin C 2%
Calcium 4%	•	Iron 10%

*Percent Daily Values are based on a 2,000 calorie diet. Your daily values may be higher or lower depending on your calorie needs.

		Calories:	2,000	2,500
Total Fat	Less than		65g	80g
Saturated Fat	Less than		20g	25g
Cholesterol	Less than		300mg	300mg
Sodium	Less than		2,400mg	2,400mg
Total Carbohydrate			300g	375g
Dietary Fiber			25g	30g

Calories per gram:
Fat 9 • Carbohydrate 4 • Protein 4

Mix all the spices together and store in an airtight container.

Yield: 2 tablespoons

CONDIMENTS

CASHEW SOUR CREAM

1 cup cashew, soaked

1/2-3/4 cup water, as needed

2 tsps freshly squeezed lemon juice

1 tsp Mother's apple cider vinegar

1/4 tsp fine grain sea salt, to taste

Nutrition Facts

Serving Size 3 tbsp (51g)
Servings Per Container 6

Amount Per Serving

Calories 110   Calories from Fat 70

	% Daily Value*
Total Fat 8g	12%
Saturated Fat 1.5g	8%
Trans Fat 0g	
Cholesterol 0mg	0%
Sodium 100mg	4%
Total Carbohydrate 6g	2%
Dietary Fiber 1g	4%
Sugars 1g	
Protein 3g	

Vitamin A 0%	•	Vitamin C 2%
Calcium 2%	•	Iron 6%

*Percent Daily Values are based on a 2,000 calorie diet. Your daily values may be higher or lower depending on your calorie needs.

		Calories:	2,000	2,500
Total Fat	Less than		65g	80g
Saturated Fat	Less than		20g	25g
Cholesterol	Less than		300mg	300mg
Sodium	Less than		2,400mg	2,400mg
Total Carbohydrate			300g	375g
Dietary Fiber			25g	30g

Calories per gram:
Fat 9 • Carbohydrate 4 • Protein 4

Fill up bowl with enough water and cover with foil. Soak cashews for a minimum of 2 hours, or up to 8 hours. Strain and rinse the cashews.

Place in the blender. Add lemon juice, vinegar, and sea salt. Add water 1 tablespoon at a time until smooth and slightly thicker consistency. Scrap down blender as needed. The cream will thicken further, as it sits.

Store in an airtight container for up to two days in the refrigerator.

Servings: 4

Target source of Dietary Fats, Protein, Iron

CLEAN MAYONNAISE

2 free-range egg yolks

1 tbsp organic Dijon Mustard, page 228, optional

3 tbsps freshly squeezed lemon juice

1 cup extra virgin olive oil

1/8 tsp fine grain sea salt

1/8 tsp ground black pepper

Nutrition Facts

Serving Size 1 tbsp (14g)
Servings Per Container 20

Amount Per Serving

Calories 100	Calories from Fat 100

	% Daily Value*
Total Fat 12g	18%
Saturated Fat 6g	30%
Trans Fat 0g	
Cholesterol 15mg	5%
Sodium 10mg	0%
Total Carbohydrate 0g	0%
Dietary Fiber 0g	0%
Sugars 0g	
Protein 0g	

Vitamin A 0%	•	Vitamin C 0%
Calcium 0%	•	Iron 0%

*Percent Daily Values are based on a 2,000 calorie diet. Your daily values may be higher or lower depending on your calorie needs.

	Calories	2,000	2,500
Total Fat	Less than	65g	80g
Saturated Fat	Less than	20g	25g
Cholesterol	Less than	300mg	300mg
Sodium	Less than	2,400mg	2,400mg
Total Carbohydrate		300g	375g
Dietary Fiber		25g	30g

Calories per gram:
Fat 9 • Carbohydrate 4 • Protein 4

Prepare Dijon Mustard.

In a small bowl, add egg yolks, Dijon mustard, and 1 teaspoon of lemon juice; whisk together well. Set food processor to LOW. Very slowly start the emulsification between the egg mixture and the oil. Dip a fork in to the oil and let it drip inside the top opening, without removing the lid.

Once the mixture begins to thicken, you can begin to add oil at a slow pace. Add a little faster as it thickens more. When the mayonnaise is thick enough, scrap from food processor and whisk in the remaining lemon juice. Taste, test and adjust you flavors. See Five Basic Tastes, page 20.

**IMPORTANT: Adding too much oil at the start can break your emulsification process. At this point, it will be hard to save and you would need to start the process over.

Yield: 1 1/4 cup

Continued on the next page.

Mayonnaise Flavor Options

All flavors should be added at the end of the emulsification process. Lightly fold flavor additions until incorporated. Before adding flavor options to the mayonnaise, process ingredients in food processor until smooth.

Bacon: 1 slice of cooked uncured, pastured bacon; reserve 1 tbsp bacon fat + crumbled bacon

Chipotle: 1/4-1/2 tsp organic chipotle powder or chili powder + 1/2 tsp maple syrup, grade B

Chive: 1/8 cup of fresh snipped chives + 2 minced garlic cloves + 1/8-1/4 tsp ground black pepper, to taste

Dill: 2 tbsps of fresh chopped dill + 1 tbsp freshly squeezed lemon juice + 1 tsp minced garlic + 1/8 tsp fine grain sea salt + 1/8 tsp of ground black pepper, to taste

Dijon: 1 1/2 tbsps Dijon mustard + 2 tbsps chopped fresh dill

Herbs: 2 1/2 tbsps of fresh mixed chopped herbs (add basil, chives, dill, oregano, parsley, tarragon or thyme)

Horseradish: 2 tbsps organic prepared horseradish + 2 tsp fresh thyme or 1/2 tsp dried thyme + fine grain sea salt and black pepper, to taste

Key Lime, Honey and Dijon mustard: 1 tbsp freshly squeezed key lime juice + 1 tbsp local raw honey + 1 tbsp Dijon mustard, page 228

Peppercorn: 1 tsp freshly ground peppercorn, or peppercorn medley + 1 tsp freshly squeezed lemon juice

Spicy: 2 organic adobo peppers + 2 tsps of organic adobo sauce (can)

Sun-Dried Tomato: 1 minced garlic clove + 1/4 cup organic sun-dried tomato.

CREAMY MUSTARD SAUCE

1/4 cup organic Dijon Mustard, page 228

1/4 cup Sour Cream, page 239

1/4 cup Clean Mayonnaise, page 225

1 tbsps dried chive

1 tsp freshly squeezed lemon juice

Nutrition Facts
Serving Size 1 1/2 tbsp (23g)
Servings Per Container 8

Amount Per Serving

Calories 80   Calories from Fat 80

% Daily Value*

Total Fat 10g	15%
Saturated Fat 5g	25%
Trans Fat 0g	
Cholesterol 10mg	3%
Sodium 90mg	4%
Total Carbohydrate 0g	0%
Dietary Fiber 0g	0%
Sugars 0g	
Protein 0g	

Vitamin A 0%	•	Vitamin C 2%
Calcium 0%	•	Iron 0%

*Percent Daily Values are based on a 2,000 calorie diet. Your daily values may be higher or lower depending on your calorie needs.

		Calories	2,000	2,500
Total Fat	Less than		65g	80g
Saturated Fat	Less than		20g	25g
Cholesterol	Less than		300mg	300mg
Sodium	Less than		2,400mg	2,400mg
Total Carbohydrate			300g	375g
Dietary Fiber			25g	30g

Calories per gram:
Fat 9 • Carbohydrate 4 • Protein 4

Prepare Dijon Mustard, Sour Cream and Clean Mayonnaise.

Combine mustard, sour cream, mayonnaise, chive and juice; mix well. Cover and chill at least one hour.

Mix well before serving.

Yield: 3/4 cup

DIJON MUSTARD

2 minced garlic clove

1 cup white wine vinegar

1 cup chopped onion

6 tbsps dry mustard, more if needed

4 drops chipotle Tabasco sauce

2 tsps fine grain sea salt

1 tbsp coconut oil, measured melted

2 tbsps local raw honey

Nutrition Facts

Serving Size 1 1/2 oz (44g)
Servings Per Container 12

Amount Per Serving

Calories 50	Calories from Fat 20

	% Daily Value*
Total Fat 2.5g	4%
Saturated Fat 1g	5%
Trans Fat 0g	
Cholesterol 0mg	0%
Sodium 390mg	16%
Total Carbohydrate 5g	2%
Dietary Fiber 1g	4%
Sugars 3g	
Protein 1g	

Vitamin A 0%	•	Vitamin C 2%
Calcium 2%	•	Iron 10%

*Percent Daily Values are based on a 2,000 calorie diet. Your daily values may be higher or lower depending on your calorie needs

	Calories	2,000	2,500
Total Fat	Less than	65g	80g
Saturated Fat	Less than	20g	25g
Cholesterol	Less than	300mg	300mg
Sodium	Less than	2,400mg	2,400mg
Total Carbohydrate		300g	375g
Dietary Fiber		25g	30g

Calories per gram:
Fat 9 • Carbohydrate 4 • Protein 4

Heat a saucepan over high heat; add garlic, white wine vinegar and onion. Bring to a boil; reduce to low heat and simmer for about 5 minutes to infuse flavors. Pour the mixture into a bowl and set aside to cool.

Heat the same saucepan over medium-high heat. Strain the vinegar mixture into the saucepan, removing garlic and onion pieces. Discard garlic and onion, or use with another dish. Add the chipotle Tabasco sauce, sea salt, oil and honey; mix well. Turn the heat to low; add the dry mustard, stirring constantly until dry mustard and vinegar mixture thickens. Do not leave the mustard at this stage; continue stirring for good consistency.

Remove the saucepan from the heat once sauce has thickened. Let cool; sauce will continue to thicken.

Tips
Keep Dijon Mustard in refrigerator for up to 2 days prior to serving, for more infused flavor.

Serve immediately or store in a non-metallic airtight container for up to 1 week. No freezer.

Servings: 6 ounces

Target source of Dietary Fats and Iron

Supportive of Immune Health

GUACAMOLE

5 ripe quartered avocados, peeled and seeded
6 tbsps chopped fresh cilantro or 6 tsps dried cilantro
3/4 cup diced red onion
4 finely diced organic jalapeno, stem and seed removed
3 tbsps freshly squeezed lime juice
1 1/2 tsps fine grain sea salt
1/2 tsp ground black pepper
2 cups shredded organic romaine lettuce, optional

Nutrition Facts

Serving Size 6 oz (185g)
Servings Per Container 10

Amount Per Serving

Calories 190	Calories from Fat 140

	% Daily Value^
Total Fat 15g	23%
Saturated Fat 3g	15%
Trans Fat 0g	
Cholesterol 0mg	0%
Sodium 350mg	15%
Total Carbohydrate 14g	5%
Dietary Fiber 9g	36%
Sugars 5g	
Protein 4g	

Vitamin A 25%	•	Vitamin C 60%
Calcium 2%	•	Iron 2%

*Percent Daily Values are based on a 2,000 calorie diet. Your daily values may be higher or lower depending on your calorie needs.

	Calories:	2,000	2,500
Total Fat	Less than	65g	80g
Saturated Fat	Less than	20g	25g
Cholesterol	Less than	300mg	300mg
Sodium	Less than	2,400mg	2,400mg
Total Carbohydrate		300g	375g
Dietary Fiber		25g	30g

Calories per gram:
Fat 9 • Carbohydrate 4 • Protein 4

In a mixing bowl, mash avocados with a fork until thin chunky. Add cilantro, red onion, jalapeno, lime juice, sea salt, and black pepper; mix well. Use a bed of lettuce with a dollop of guacamole, as a plate salad or dig in as a dip.

Tips

Soft Avocado – gentle pressure, eat within 2 days.

Firm Avocado – can take up to 5 days to ripen.

To store Avocado, remove the seed, squeeze a little citrus juice and wrap tightly with plastic wrap. Do not touch with finger.

Servings: 10

Target source of Vitamin A, Vitamin C, Folate, Pantothenic Acid, Copper, Potassium, Magnesium, Dietary Fats, Dietary Fiber

Supportive of Immune and Detoxification Health

232.

HONEY CINNAMON ALMOND BUTTER

3/4 cup almond butter

1/2 cup local raw honey

1 tsp ground cinnamon

Nutrition Facts

Serving Size 2 tbsp (45g)
Servings Per Container 8

Amount Per Serving

Calories 210   Calories from Fat 120

	% Daily Value*
Total Fat 13g	20%
Saturated Fat 1.5g	8%
Trans Fat 0g	
Cholesterol 0mg	0%
Sodium 55mg	2%
Total Carbohydrate 22g	7%
Dietary Fiber 3g	12%
Sugars 17g	
Protein 5g	

Vitamin A 0%	•	Vitamin C 0%
Calcium 8%	•	Iron 6%

*Percent Daily Values are based on a 2,000 calorie diet. Your daily values may be higher or lower depending on your calorie needs

	Calories	2,000	2,500
Total Fat	Less than	65g	80g
Saturated Fat	Less than	20g	25g
Cholesterol	Less than	300mg	300mg
Sodium	Less than	2,400mg	2,400mg
Total Carbohydrate		300g	375g
Dietary Fiber		25g	30g

Calories per gram
Fat 9 • Carbohydrate 4 • Protein 4

Combine all ingredients; mix thoroughly.

Tip
Use it as a substitution for peanut butter, except it's healthier.

Yield: 1 cup

Target source of Protein, Dietary Fats, Vitamins B2, B3, Folate

Supportive of Immune and Detoxification Health

KETCHUP

1/4 cup ground dry mustard
1/8 cup white wine vinegar
1/4 cup water
1 1/2 tbsps maple syrup, grade B
1/4 tsp iodized sea salt

Nutrition Facts		
Serving Size (157g)		
Servings Per Container		
Amount Per Serving		
Calories 260	Calories from Fat 100	
		% Daily Value*
Total Fat 11g		**17%**
Saturated Fat 0g		**0%**
Trans Fat 0g		
Cholesterol 0mg		**0%**
Sodium 590mg		**25%**
Total Carbohydrate 29g		**10%**
Dietary Fiber 5g		**20%**
Sugars 20g		
Protein 10g		
Vitamin A 0%	•	Vitamin C 4%
Calcium 15%	•	Iron 100%
*Percent Daily Values are based on a 2,000 calorie diet. Your daily values may be higher or lower depending on your calorie needs		

	Calories	2,000	2,500
Total Fat	Less than	65g	80g
Saturated Fat	Less than	20g	25g
Cholesterol	Less than	300mg	300mg
Sodium	Less than	2,400mg	2,400mg
Total Carbohydrate		300g	375g
Dietary Fiber		25g	30g

Calories per gram:
Fat 9 • Carbohydrate 4 • Protein 4

Heat a saucepan over medium heat; add mustard, vinegar, water, maple syrup and sea salt.

Simmer over medium heat, whisking until thickened, about 3 to 5 minutes. Remove from the stove and let cool.

Store in the refrigerator in an airtight container for up to 1 month.

Yield: 1/2 cup

PICKLED GINGER

8 ounces of fresh ginger root, peeled and cut into smaller
  pieces
1 1/2 tsps sea salt
1/4 tsp sesame oil
1 cup Mothers apple cider vinegar
1/3 cup coconut sugar

Nutrition Facts

Serving Size 1/2 oz (16g)
Servings Per Container 33

Amount Per Serving

Calories 15	Calories from Fat 0

	% Daily Value*
Total Fat 0g	0%
Saturated Fat 0g	0%
Trans Fat 0g	
Cholesterol 0mg	0%
Sodium 105mg	4%
Total Carbohydrate 3g	1%
Dietary Fiber 0g	0%
Sugars 2g	
Protein 0g	

Vitamin A 0%	•	Vitamin C 0%
Calcium 0%	•	Iron 0%

*Percent Daily Values are based on a 2,000 calorie diet. Your daily values may be higher or lower depending on your calorie needs.

	Calories	2,000	2,500
Total Fat	Less than	65g	80g
Saturated Fat	Less than	20g	25g
Cholesterol	Less than	300mg	300mg
Sodium	Less than	2,400mg	2,400mg
Total Carbohydrate		300g	375g
Dietary Fiber		25g	30g

Calories per gram:
Fat 9 • Carbohydrate 4 • Protein 4

Combine pieces of ginger, sea salt and sesame oil in a mixing bowl; mix well. Transfer to a clean mason jar and let refrigerate for 30 minutes.

Heat a skillet over medium-high heat. Add vinegar and coconut sugar; stir until dissolved. Coconut sugar will still have a grainy texture. Bring to almost boiling, and then pour into the jar over the ginger pieces. Glass will be hot. Cover jar with a paper towel and allow the mixture to cool. Once liquid is cool, place the lid on the jar and place it back in the refrigerator.

Store jar in the refrigerator for up to one week.

Tips
Ginger will change colors because of the vinegar; greenish

If you choose to buy pickled ginger from a store, be sure of the 'sugar' added ingredients that go into keeping this product on the shelf.

It should be minimal with no natural or artificial flavorings; just basic ingredients, like this recipe.

ROASTED GARLIC

6 whole garlic clove, pressed slightly

2-3 tbsps extra virgin olive oil

Preheat oven to 375° F.

Cut off the top portion of the garlic head so that cloves are showing. Peel off outer layer by rubbing garlic lightly with fingers. Brush 2 teaspoons of oil on top of each garlic head and let it soak for 7-10 minutes.

Cover garlic clove with aluminum foil and place in an oven safe baking dish. Bake for 45 minutes until golden brown.

Let garlic cool, unwrap and squeeze from the bottom to remove roasted cloves.

Servings: 6

Supportive of Immune Health

Nutrition Facts	
Serving Size 1 clove (10g)	
Servings Per Container 6	

Amount Per Serving	
Calories 60	Calories from Fat 60

	% Daily Value*
Total Fat 7g	11%
Saturated Fat 1g	5%
Trans Fat 0g	
Cholesterol 0mg	0%
Sodium 0mg	0%
Total Carbohydrate 1g	0%
Dietary Fiber 0g	0%
Sugars 0g	
Protein 0g	

Vitamin A 0%	•	Vitamin C 2%
Calcium 0%	•	Iron 0%

*Percent Daily Values are based on a 2,000 calorie diet. Your daily values may be higher or lower depending on your calorie needs.

	Calories	2,000	2,500
Total Fat	Less than	65g	80g
Saturated Fat	Less than	20g	25g
Cholesterol	Less than	300mg	300mg
Sodium	Less than	2,400mg	2,400mg
Total Carbohydrate		300g	375g
Dietary Fiber		25g	30g

Calories per gram:
Fat 9 • Carbohydrate 4 • Protein 4

SOUR CREAM

1/2 cup Clean Mayonnaise, page 225

1/2 cup coconut milk, full fat (in a can)

1/2 tsp Mother's apple cider vinegar

1 finely minced garlic clove

Nutrition Facts

Serving Size 1 Tbsp (15g)
Servings Per Container 16

Amount Per Serving

Calories 60	Calories from Fat 60

	% Daily Value*
Total Fat 7g	11%
Saturated Fat 4g	20%
Trans Fat 0g	
Cholesterol 10mg	3%
Sodium 5mg	0%
Total Carbohydrate 0g	0%
Dietary Fiber 0g	0%
Sugars 0g	
Protein 0g	

Vitamin A 0%	•	Vitamin C 0%
Calcium 0%	•	Iron 2%

*Percent Daily Values are based on a 2,000 calorie diet. Your daily values may be higher or lower depending on your calorie needs.

	Calories	2,000	2,500
Total Fat	Less than	65g	80g
Saturated Fat	Less than	20g	25g
Cholesterol	Less than	300mg	300mg
Sodium	Less than	2,400mg	2,400mg
Total Carbohydrate		300g	375g
Dietary Fiber		25g	30g

Calories per gram
Fat 9 • Carbohydrate 4 • Protein 4

Prepare Clean Mayonnaise.

Place full fat coconut milk in refrigerator, upside down allowing for the fat to separate from the coconut juice; for a minimum of 1 hour.

Mix mayonnaise, coconut fat (not juice), vinegar and garlic and whisk. Refrigerate for 30 min or longer to thicken.

Servings: 4

240.

TOASTED NUTS

Preheat oven to 400° F.

Use the amount called for in the recipe.

Add your choice of nuts to a sheet pan and toast in the oven for 7-10 minutes until lightly golden and fragrant; stirring occasionally. Turn the pan around half way through, to keep an even toast. Remove and set aside to cool for a few minutes.

Alternatively, you can place the nuts in a skillet over medium-high heat; stirring frequently, to prevent burning.

Tip
Nuts can burn quickly because the nuts natural oils are released.

CHUTNEY

CRANBERRY AND APRICOT CHUTNEY

1 1/4 cups coconut sugar

1/2 cup water

3 cups dried cranberry

3/4 cup snipped dried apricot

3 tbsps Mother's apple cider vinegar

1 tbsp minced fresh ginger

3 tbsps local raw honey

Nutrition Facts

Serving Size 2 tbsp (66g)
Servings Per Container 14

Amount Per Serving

Calories 180	Calories from Fat 0

	% Daily Value*
Total Fat 0g	0%
Saturated Fat 0g	0%
Trans Fat 0g	
Cholesterol 0mg	0%
Sodium 40mg	2%
Total Carbohydrate 46g	15%
Dietary Fiber 2g	8%
Sugars 42g	
Protein 0g	

Vitamin A 2%	•	Vitamin C 25%
Calcium 0%	•	Iron 2%

*Percent Daily Values are based on a 2,000 calorie diet. Your daily values may be higher or lower depending on your calorie needs

	Calories	2,000	2,500
Total Fat	Less than	65g	80g
Saturated Fat	Less than	20g	25g
Cholesterol	Less than	300mg	300mg
Sodium	Less than	2,400mg	2,400mg
Total Carbohydrate		300g	375g
Dietary Fiber		25g	30g

Calories per gram:
Fat 9 • Carbohydrate 4 • Protein 4

Heat a saucepan over medium-high heat; boil coconut sugar and water until sugar is dissolved; stirring occasionally.

Add cranberry, apricot, vinegar, ginger and honey. Reduce heat and simmer for 5 minutes until cranberry has popped and mixture starts to thicken, stirring occasionally. Remove from heat and allow cooling.

Bring to room temperature 30 minutes before serving; refrigerate up to four days. Reheat on medium-low heat for 3-5 minutes.

Servings: 14, Yield 2 tbsps each

Target source of Dietary Fiber and Vitamin C

Supportive of Immune and Gut Health

FIG AND APPLE CHUTNEY

1 cup coconut sugar

2 1/2 cups Mother's apple cider vinegar

1/2 cup minced green onion

1/4 cup minced ginger, peeled

1 1/2 tsps dry yellow mustard seed

2 tbsps lemon zest

3/4 tsp fine grain sea salt

1/2 tsp freshly ground pepper

1 organic chopped organic apple, about 1 cup

1 1/2 cups halved fresh firm fig, no stem or 1 cup unsweetened
   dried fig

2 tbsps chopped parsley, garnish

Nutrition Facts

Serving Size 1/2 cup (155g)
Servings Per Container 8

Amount Per Serving

Calories 170   Calories from Fat 5

% Daily Value*

Total Fat 0g	0%
Saturated Fat 0g	0%
Trans Fat 0g	
Cholesterol 0mg	0%
Sodium 260mg	11%
Total Carbohydrate 46g	15%
Dietary Fiber 1g	4%
Sugars 30g	
Protein 1g	

Vitamin A 8% • Vitamin C 30%

Calcium 0% • Iron 2%

*Percent Daily Values are based on a 2,000 calorie diet. Your daily values may be higher or lower depending on your calorie needs.

	Calories	2,000	2,500
Total Fat	Less than	65g	80g
Saturated Fat	Less than	20g	25g
Cholesterol	Less than	300mg	300mg
Sodium	Less than	2,400mg	2,400mg
Total Carbohydrate		300g	375g
Dietary Fiber		25g	30g

Calories per gram:
Fat 9 • Carbohydrate 4 • Protein 4

In a small bowl, combine sugar, vinegar, green onion, ginger, mustard seed, lemon zest, sea salt and black pepper; bring to a boil. Reduce heat to a simmer and reduce liquid by 2/3; sauce will thicken.

Softly cook the fig and apple, until figs begin to soften; about 30 minutes.

Tip
Sweet fig provides a satisfying complement to the savory steak or bird.

Yield: 1/4 cup

Target source of Vitamin A, Vitamin C, Vitamin K, Potassium

Supportive of Immune Health

HONEY MAPLE CHUTNEY

1 cup local raw honey

3/4 cup Mother's apple cider vinegar

1/2 tsp ground cinnamon

1 cup chopped mango, peeled and seeded

3/4 cup chopped raisin

3/4 cup chopped onion

1/2 cup chopped organic red bell pepper

1/2 cup chopped unsweetened dried dates

1 chopped organic apple, peeled; about 3/4 cup

1 finely chopped garlic clove

Nutrition Facts		
Serving Size 4 1/2 oz (130g)		
Servings Per Container 10		
Amount Per Serving		
Calories 200	Calories from Fat 0	
		% Daily Value*
Total Fat 0g		0%
Saturated Fat 0g		0%
Trans Fat 0g		
Cholesterol 0mg		0%
Sodium 5mg		0%
Total Carbohydrate 53g		18%
Dietary Fiber 3g		12%
Sugars 45g		
Protein 1g		
Vitamin A 10%	•	Vitamin C 40%
Calcium 2%	•	Iron 4%

*Percent Daily Values are based on a 2,000 calorie diet. Your daily values may be higher or lower depending on your calorie needs

	Calories	2,000	2,500
Total Fat	Less than	65g	80g
Saturated Fat	Less than	20g	25g
Cholesterol	Less than	300mg	300mg
Sodium	Less than	2,400mg	2,400mg
Total Carbohydrate		300g	375g
Dietary Fiber		25g	30g

Calories per gram:
Fat 9 • Carbohydrate 4 • Protein 4

Combine honey, vinegar and cinnamon and set aside.

Heat a skillet over high heat. Add mango, raisin, onion, bell pepper, dates, apple and garlic. Bring to a boil, and then decrease heat to medium-high, simmer and sauté for about 40 minutes or until crisp tender; stirring occasionally.

Tips
If mangos are not available, you can substitute 2 apples or 1 papaya

Cool and store in an airtight container for up to 7 days.

Yield: 4 1/4 cups

RASPBERRY HONEY NUT CHUTNEY

1/2 cup cashew

1/2 cup Clean Mayonnaise, page 225

1/4 cup Honey Maple Chutney, page 246

2 tbsps coconut sugar

2 tbsps raspberry balsamic vinegar

1 tsp organic curry powder

Nutrition Facts

Serving Size 1 oz (36g)
Servings Per Container 8

Amount Per Serving

Calories 180   Calories from Fat 140

% Daily Value*

Total Fat 16g	25%
Saturated Fat 7g	35%
Trans Fat 0g	
Cholesterol 15mg	5%
Sodium 15mg	1%
Total Carbohydrate 10g	3%
Dietary Fiber 1g	4%
Sugars 6g	
Protein 2g	

Vitamin A 2%	•	Vitamin C 4%
Calcium 0%	•	Iron 4%

*Percent Daily Values are based on a 2,000 calorie diet. Your daily values may be higher or lower depending on your calorie needs:

		Calories	2,000	2,500
Total Fat	Less than		65g	80g
Saturated Fat	Less than		20g	25g
Cholesterol	Less than		300mg	300mg
Sodium	Less than		2,400mg	2,400mg
Total Carbohydrate			300g	375g
Dietary Fiber			25g	30g

Calories per gram
Fat 9 • Carbohydrate 4 • Protein 4

Prepare Clean Mayonnaise and Honey Maple Chutney.

Combine cashew, mayonnaise, honey maple chutney, coconut sugar, vinegar and curry powder; mix until smooth.

Yield: 1 1/4 cups

SAUCES

BASIC TOMATO SAUCE OR PIZZA SAUCE

1 tbsp extra virgin olive oil

1 cup chopped onion

1 tbsp chopped fresh basil or 1 tsp dried basil

2 chopped garlic clove

2 cups organic diced tomato

1 organic tomato paste, 6 oz can

2 tsps Italian Seasoning, page 213

2 bay leaves

1/4 tsp fine grain sea salt

1/4 tsp ground black pepper

Nutrition Facts

Serving Size 4 oz (106g)
Servings Per Container 8

Amount Per Serving

Calories 60	Calories from Fat 15

	% Daily Value*
Total Fat 2g	3%
Saturated Fat 0g	0%
Trans Fat 0g	
Cholesterol 0mg	0%
Sodium 190mg	8%
Total Carbohydrate 9g	3%
Dietary Fiber 1g	4%
Sugars 4g	
Protein 1g	

Vitamin A 10%	•	Vitamin C 30%
Calcium 4%	•	Iron 6%

*Percent Daily Values are based on a 2,000 calorie diet. Your daily values may be higher or lower depending on your calorie needs.

		Calories	2,000	2,500
Total Fat	Less than		65g	80g
Saturated Fat	Less than		20g	25g
Cholesterol	Less than		300mg	300mg
Sodium	Less than		2,400mg	2,400mg
Total Carbohydrate			300g	375g
Dietary Fiber			25g	30g

Calories per gram:
Fat 9 • Carbohydrate 4 • Protein 4

Prepare Italian Seasoning.

Heat a medium saucepan over low heat. Add oil, onion, basil and garlic; stir often, about 6 to 8 minutes until onion is translucent.

In a food processor or blender, puree the tomato and tomato paste. Add contents to the onion mixture and bring to a simmer over medium-high heat. Reduce the heat to low and let the sauce simmer slowly, covered, for 30 minutes; stirring the bottom often to prevent burning. Remove the bay leaves before serving; season with sea salt and black pepper. Remove bay leaves before serving.

Servings: 8

Target source of Vitamin C

Supportive of Immune Health

BASTING SAUCE

2 cups Mother's apple cider vinegar

1/2 tsp garlic powder

1/2 tsp Poultry Seasoning, page 217

3 bay leaves

1/2 tsp crushed organic red pepper flake

1/2 tbsp chopped fresh thyme or 1/2 tsp crushed dried thyme

1/2 tbsp chopped fresh rosemary or 1/2 tsp crushed dried
   rosemary

1/2 tsp Lemon Pepper Seasoning, page 215

Nutrition Facts

Serving Size 1 tbsp (10g)
Servings Per Container 48

Amount Per Serving

Calories 5	Calories from Fat 0

% Daily Value*

Total Fat 0g	0%
Saturated Fat 0g	0%
Trans Fat 0g	
Cholesterol 0mg	0%
Sodium 0mg	0%
Total Carbohydrate 1g	0%
Dietary Fiber 0g	0%
Sugars 0g	
Protein 0g	

Vitamin A 0%	•	Vitamin C 0%
Calcium 0%	•	Iron 0%

*Percent Daily Values are based on a 2,000 calorie diet. Your daily values may be higher or lower depending on your calorie needs:

	Calories	2,000	2,500
Total Fat	Less than	65g	80g
Saturated Fat	Less than	20g	25g
Cholesterol	Less than	300mg	300mg
Sodium	Less than	2,400mg	2,400mg
Total Carbohydrate		300g	375g
Dietary Fiber		25g	30g

Calories per gram:
Fat 9 • Carbohydrate 4 • Protein 4

Prepare Poultry Seasoning and Lemon Pepper Seasoning.

Heat all ingredients in a saucepan over high heat; mix well. Bring to a rolling boil. Remove from the stove and cover. Let the mixture cool completely.

Servings: 8

Target source of Vitamin K

BBQ SAUCE

1/2 tsp ground organic cayenne

1 tsp ground cumin

1 tbsp coconut sugar

1/2 tsp fine grain sea salt

1/2 tsp ground black pepper

Water, as needed to loosen

Nutrition Facts

Serving Size 1 1/2 oz (40g)
Servings Per Container 8

Amount Per Serving

Calories 60	Calories from Fat 0

	% Daily Value*
Total Fat 0g	0%
Saturated Fat 0g	0%
Trans Fat 0g	
Cholesterol 0mg	0%
Sodium 370mg	15%
Total Carbohydrate 14g	5%
Dietary Fiber 1g	4%
Sugars 10g	
Protein 1g	

Vitamin A 8%	•	Vitamin C 8%
Calcium 2%	•	Iron 4%

*Percent Daily Values are based on a 2,000 calorie diet. Your daily values may be higher or lower depending on your calorie needs.

	Calories	2,000	2,500
Total Fat	Less than	65g	80g
Saturated Fat	Less than	20g	25g
Cholesterol	Less than	300mg	300mg
Sodium	Less than	2,400mg	2,400mg
Total Carbohydrate		300g	375g
Dietary Fiber		25g	30g

Calories per gram:
Fat 9 • Carbohydrate 4 • Protein 4

Loosen the tomato paste in a medium skillet over medium heat; stirring often to help break up.

Mix honey, vinegar, coconut aminos and Tabasco sauce in a small bowl; mix well. In a separate bowl, combine garlic, onion, paprika, garlic powder, onion powder, chipotle powder, chili powder, cayenne, cumin, coconut sugar, sea salt and black pepper; mix well.

Add wet to dry ingredients; mix well. Heat a skillet over high heat and add mixture. Bring to a boil; reduce to a simmer and cook for 5 minutes. Remove the skillet from the heat, cover and keep warm, to let sauce cool and thicken.

Servings: 4

Supportive of Gut Health

BÉARNAISE SAUCE

1/2 cup white wine

1 tbsp finely chopped shallot

1/2 tsp chopped fresh tarragon, to taste

3-4 free-range egg yolks

1/2 tsp fine grain sea salt

1/2 cup Clarified Butter, page 203

2-3 tbsps coconut milk, full fat

Nutrition Facts		
Serving Size 3 oz (88g)		
Servings Per Container 4		
Amount Per Serving		
Calories 360	Calories from Fat 310	
		% Daily Value*
Total Fat 35g		54%
Saturated Fat 22g		110%
Trans Fat 0g		
Cholesterol 265mg		88%
Sodium 300mg		13%
Total Carbohydrate 2g		1%
Dietary Fiber 0g		0%
Sugars 0g		
Protein 3g		
Vitamin A 25%	•	Vitamin C 0%
Calcium 2%	•	Iron 4%

*Percent Daily Values are based on a 2,000 calorie diet. Your daily values may be higher or lower depending on your calorie needs.

	Calories	2,000	2,500
Total Fat	Less than	65g	80g
Saturated Fat	Less than	20g	25g
Cholesterol	Less than	300mg	300mg
Sodium	Less than	2,400mg	2,400mg
Total Carbohydrate		300g	375g
Dietary Fiber		25g	30g

Calories per gram:
Fat 9 • Carbohydrate 4 • Protein 4

Prepare Clarified Butter.

Combine wine, shallot and tarragon; sauté until wine is reduced to a glaze.

Combine egg yolks and sea salt in a blender. Slowly add glaze to blender and pulse while it pours. Heat the clarified butter in a saucepan on high heat; bring to a boil. Pour in the clarified butter steadily, with blender on low, until the sauce thickens. Remove, scrape down sides and add to your dish.

Tip
Clarified butter is great for high temperature cooking.

Servings: 4

Target source of Iodine, Selenium, Phosphorus, Vitamin D, B Vitamins, Dietary Fats

Supportive of Immune and Detoxification Health

BELL PEPPER, GARLIC AND TURKEY SPAGHETTI SAUCE

2 tbsps extra virgin olive oil, divided
1/2 lb free-range, pastured ground turkey
3/4 cup chopped onion
1/3 cup chopped organic green bell pepper, seeds and ribs
   removed
2 tbsps crushed garlic clove
3 cups chopped organic plum tomato, with juice
1 tbsp chopped fresh oregano or 1 tsp dried oregano
1/4 tsp fine grain sea salt
1/4 tsp ground black pepper

Nutrition Facts
Serving Size 3 oz (87g)
Servings Per Container 8

Amount Per Serving

Calories 90   Calories from Fat 45

% Daily Value*

Total Fat 5g — 8%
Saturated Fat 1g — 5%
Trans Fat 0g
Cholesterol 15mg — 5%
Sodium 95mg — 4%
Total Carbohydrate 4g — 1%
Dietary Fiber 1g — 4%
Sugars 2g
Protein 7g

Vitamin A 6% • Vitamin C 20%
Calcium 2% • Iron 2%

*Percent Daily Values are based on a 2,000 calorie diet. Your daily values may be higher or lower depending on your calorie needs.

	Calories	2,000	2,500
Total Fat	Less than	65g	80g
Saturated Fat	Less than	20g	25g
Cholesterol	Less than	300mg	300mg
Sodium	Less than	2,400mg	2,400mg
Total Carbohydrate		300g	375g
Dietary Fiber		25g	30g

Calories per gram:
Fat 9 • Carbohydrate 4 • Protein 4

Heat 1 tablespoon of oil in a skillet over medium-high heat. Add turkey and cook, about 5-8 minutes; stirring often, no pink. Strain turkey grease, cover and set aside. Discard turkey grease.

Add the remaining 1 tablespoon of oil; sauté onion, bell pepper and garlic for about 5 minutes. Add turkey, plum tomato with juice, oregano, sea salt and black pepper. Break up tomato with a wooden spoon. Gently simmer for about 20 minutes over medium-high heat, uncovered; stirring often.

Tip
Add a little flavor by using this recipe when you need a spaghetti sauce or need to add additional protein.

Servings: 8

Target source of Vitamin A, Vitamin B6, Vitamin C, Protein

Supportive of Immune Health

CHERRY WALNUT TOPPING

2 cups chopped walnut or pecan

1 cup dried tart cherry

2 tbsps coconut aminos

1/2 tsp garlic powder

1/2 tsp Seasoning Salt, page 219

1/2 tsp ground cumin

1/4 tsp ground organic cayenne pepper, to taste

1 tbsp coconut oil

Nutrition Facts

Serving Size 2 oz (50g)
Servings Per Container 8

Amount Per Serving

Calories 250   Calories from Fat 180

% Daily Value*

Total Fat 20g	31%
Saturated Fat 2.5g	13%
Trans Fat 0g	
Cholesterol 0mg	0%
Sodium 135mg	6%
Total Carbohydrate 17g	6%
Dietary Fiber 6g	24%
Sugars 8g	
Protein 5g	

Vitamin A 10% • Vitamin C 0%

Calcium 4% • Iron 8%

*Percent Daily Values are based on a 2,000 calorie diet. Your daily values may be higher or lower depending on your calorie needs.

		2,000	2,500
Total Fat	Less than	65g	80g
Saturated Fat	Less than	20g	25g
Cholesterol	Less than	300mg	300mg
Sodium	Less than	2,400mg	2,400mg
Total Carbohydrate		300g	375g
Dietary Fiber		25g	30g

Calories per gram
Fat 9 • Carbohydrate 4 • Protein 4

Prepare Seasoning Salt.

Combine walnut and cherry in a medium bowl. In a separate bowl, combine coconut aminos, garlic powder, seasoned salt, cumin and red pepper; mix well. Pour over walnut mixture; stir to coat.

Heat 1 tablespoon of oil in a large skillet over medium heat. Add walnut mixture; sauté for 3-4 minutes until walnuts are light brown, stirring constantly to prevent burning. Add more oil, if needed. Remove from heat. Spread on waxed paper or aluminum foil to cool.

Tip
Store in an airtight in the refrigerator up to 2 days.

Yield: 3 cups

Target source of Copper, Manganese, Dietary Fats, Dietary Fiber

Supportive of Immune Health

CHILI SAUCE

6 oz organic tomato sauce

2 tbsps organic tomato paste

1 1/2 tbsps freshly squeezed lemon juice

2 tbsps coconut sugar

1/4 tsp ground mustard

1/4 tsp onion powder

1/4 tsp garlic powder

1/4 tsp organic chili powder

2 dashes coconut aminos

Nutrition Facts

Serving Size 1oz (28g)
Servings Per Container 9

Amount Per Serving

Calories 30	Calories from Fat 5

	% Daily Value*
Total Fat 0.5g	1%
Saturated Fat 0g	0%
Trans Fat 0g	
Cholesterol 0mg	0%
Sodium 110mg	5%
Total Carbohydrate 5g	2%
Dietary Fiber 0g	0%
Sugars 4g	
Protein 0g	

Vitamin A 4%	•	Vitamin C 6%
Calcium 0%	•	Iron 2%

*Percent Daily Values are based on a 2,000 calorie diet. Your daily values may be higher or lower depending on your calorie needs.

		Calories	2,000	2,500
Total Fat	Less than		65g	80g
Saturated Fat	Less than		20g	25g
Cholesterol	Less than		300mg	300mg
Sodium	Less than		2,400mg	2,400mg
Total Carbohydrate			300g	375g
Dietary Fiber			25g	30g

Calories per gram
Fat 9 • Carbohydrate 4 • Protein 4

Combine all ingredients in a mixing bowl; whisk until incorporated.

Place in the refrigerator a couple of hours before use, to set.

Yield: 9 ounces

Tip
Store chili sauce in the refrigerator in an airtight container for up to one week.

CILANTRO-AVOCADO CREAM SAUCE

1/4 cup avocado

2 tbsps water

2-3 tbsps freshly squeezed lime juice

1 tsp Mother's apple cider vinegar

1 cup packed fresh cilantro

1 tsp fine grain sea salt

1 tsp ground black pepper

1/2 tsp garlic powder

3/4 tsp ground cumin

1/8-1/4 tsp ground organic cayenne

Nutrition Facts

Serving Size 1oz (29g)
Servings Per Container 9

Amount Per Serving

Calories 35	Calories from Fat 30

% Daily Value*

Total Fat 3g	5%
Saturated Fat 0g	0%
Trans Fat 0g	
Cholesterol 0mg	0%
Sodium 260mg	11%
Total Carbohydrate 3g	1%
Dietary Fiber 2g	8%
Sugars 0g	
Protein 1g	

Vitamin A 4%	•	Vitamin C 6%
Calcium 0%	•	Iron 2%

*Percent Daily Values are based on a 2,000 calorie diet. Your daily values may be higher or lower depending on your calorie needs.

	Calories	2,000	2,500
Total Fat	Less than	65g	80g
Saturated Fat	Less than	20g	25g
Cholesterol	Less than	300mg	300mg
Sodium	Less than	2,400mg	2,400mg
Total Carbohydrate		300g	375g
Dietary Fiber		25g	30g

Calories per gram
Fat 9 • Carbohydrate 4 • Protein 4

Cut avocado in half, lengthwise. Remove seed and spoon avocado into food processor. Add in water 1 tbsp at a time, until creamy.

Add lime juice, vinegar, cilantro, sea salt and black pepper, garlic powder, ground cumin and cayenne. Process until smooth and well blended. Use immediately for best results.

Tip
Press a piece of plastic wrap onto cream sauce, inside a container with lid for up to 2 days. This will help keep it from browning.

Yield: 1 1/4 cup

Target source of Vitamin A, Vitamin C, Dietary Fiber

Supportive of Immune Health

CRANBERRY SAUCE WITH LIME AND GINGER

1/2 cup water

1/2 cup coconut sugar

1/2 cup maple syrup, grade B

1 1/2 tsps finely zested lime

2 tbsps freshly squeezed lime juice

1 cup dried cranberry

1 tsp minced fresh ginger

Nutrition Facts
Serving Size 2 oz (67g)
Servings Per Container 8

Amount Per Serving

Calories 150	Calories from Fat 0

	% Daily Value*
Total Fat 0g	0%
Saturated Fat 0g	0%
Trans Fat 0g	
Cholesterol 0mg	0%
Sodium 30mg	1%
Total Carbohydrate 37g	12%
Dietary Fiber 1g	4%
Sugars 36g	
Protein 0g	

Vitamin A 2%	•	Vitamin C 20%
Calcium 2%	•	Iron 0%

*Percent Daily Values are based on a 2,000 calorie diet. Your daily values may be higher or lower depending on your calorie needs.

	Calories	2,000	2,500
Total Fat	Less than	65g	80g
Saturated Fat	Less than	20g	25g
Cholesterol	Less than	300mg	300mg
Sodium	Less than	2,400mg	2,400mg
Total Carbohydrate		300g	375g
Dietary Fiber		25g	30g

Calories per gram:
Fat 9 • Carbohydrate 4 • Protein 4

Heat a saucepan over high heat. Add water, coconut sugar, maple syrup, lime peel, and lime juice. Bring to boil; reduce heat and simmer for 3 minutes until sugar has dissolved.

Add cranberry; simmer for 5 minutes, stirring occasionally. Add ginger; simmer for an additional 6 minutes, stirring occasionally until cranberry has popped and mixture begins to thicken. Remove from heat and let cool slightly.

Yield: 2 1/3 cup

Target source of Vitamin C

Supportive of Immune Health

CREAMY MAPLE AND TAHINI SAUCE

1 tbsp tahini sauce

1 tbsp maple syrup, grade B

2 tsps freshly squeezed lemon juice

1/4 tsp garlic powder

1/8 tsp fine grain sea salt

1/8 tsp ground black pepper

Combine all ingredients and mix well.

Servings: 4

Nutrition Facts

Serving Size 2 tbsp (35g)
Servings Per Container 1

Amount Per Serving

Calories 110	Calories from Fat 80

	% Daily Value*
Total Fat 9g	**14%**
Saturated Fat 1g	**5%**
Trans Fat 0g	
Cholesterol 0mg	**0%**
Sodium 580mg	**24%**
Total Carbohydrate 8g	**3%**
Dietary Fiber 2g	**8%**
Sugars 4g	
Protein 3g	

Vitamin A 0%	•	Vitamin C 6%
Calcium 4%	•	Iron 4%

*Percent Daily Values are based on a 2,000 calorie diet. Your daily values may be higher or lower depending on your calorie needs.

	Calories	2,000	2,500
Total Fat	Less than	65g	80g
Saturated Fat	Less than	20g	25g
Cholesterol	Less than	300mg	300mg
Sodium	Less than	2,400mg	2,400mg
Total Carbohydrate		300g	375g
Dietary Fiber		25g	30g

Calories per gram:
Fat 9 • Carbohydrate 4 • Protein 4

ENCHILADA SAUCE

1 dried organic adobo peppers

1 cup organic vegetable broth

1/4 white onion, wedges

2 crushed garlic clove

1/2 tsp organic chili powder

1/2 tsp ground cumin

1 tsp fine grain sea salt

1 tsp ground black pepper

Nutrition Facts
Serving Size 2 1/2oz (71g)
Servings Per Container 4

Amount Per Serving

Calories 15   Calories from Fat 5

% Daily Value*

Total Fat 0g   0%

Saturated Fat 0g   0%

Trans Fat 0g

Cholesterol 0mg   0%

Sodium 750mg   31%

Total Carbohydrate 3g   1%

Dietary Fiber 1g   4%

Sugars 1g

Protein 1g

Vitamin A 10%   •   Vitamin C 4%

Calcium 0%   •   Iron 2%

*Percent Daily Values are based on a 2,000 calorie diet. Your daily values may be higher or lower depending on your calorie needs.

	Calories	2,000	2,500
Total Fat	Less than	65g	80g
Saturated Fat	Less than	20g	25g
Cholesterol	Less than	300mg	300mg
Sodium	Less than	2,400mg	2,400mg
Total Carbohydrate		300g	375g
Dietary Fiber		25g	30g

Calories per gram:
Fat 9   •   Carbohydrate 4   •   Protein 4

Deseed Adobo peppers; do not rinse. Adobo peppers are not hot, just flavorful.

Heat the vegetable broth in a saucepan over high heat; bring to a boil. Add peppers in vegetable broth, about 7-10 minutes, until soft. Add adobo pepper, vegetable broth, onion, garlic, chili powder, cumin, sea salt and black pepper to a food processor; blend to incorporate. Add 1 tablespoon of water at a time, as needed to reach desired consistency.

Servings: 4

Supportive of Detoxification Health

GINGER-DILL GLAZE SAUCE

4 tbsps Mother's apple cider vinegar; plus1 tsp

1 1/2 tsp chopped dill weed

1 tbsp extra virgin olive oil

1 1/2 tsps ground ginger

1/4 tsp fine sea salt

1 1/2 tbsps sesame oil

2 1/4 tbsps organic ginger spread

Nutrition Facts

Serving Size 2 tbsp (39g)
Servings Per Container 4

Amount Per Serving

Calories 120   Calories from Fat 80

	% Daily Value*
Total Fat 9g	14%
Saturated Fat 1.5g	8%
Trans Fat 0g	
Cholesterol 0mg	0%
Sodium 150mg	6%
Total Carbohydrate 12g	4%
Dietary Fiber 0g	0%
Sugars 9g	
Protein 0g	

Vitamin A 0% • Vitamin C 0%

Calcium 0% • Iron 0%

*Percent Daily Values are based on a 2,000 calorie diet. Your daily values may be higher or lower depending on your calorie needs.

	Calories	2,000	2,500
Total Fat	Less than	65g	80g
Saturated Fat	Less than	20g	25g
Cholesterol	Less than	300mg	300mg
Sodium	Less than	2,400mg	2,400mg
Total Carbohydrate		300g	375g
Dietary Fiber		25g	30g

Calories per gram:
Fat 9 • Carbohydrate 4 • Protein 4

In a bowl, combine apple cider vinegar, dill, oil, ginger, sea salt, sesame oil and organic ginger spread; mix to incorporate and set aside.

Tip
Store in the refrigerator in an airtight container for up to 4 days.

Yield: 1/3 cup

Supportive of Immune Health

NIGHTSHADE FREE TOMATO SAUCE

2 1/2 cups steamed organic carrot

1/3 cup steamed beet

2/3 cup water

2 tbsps extra virgin olive oil

3/4 cup chopped onion

1 minced garlic clove

2 tbsps freshly squeezed lemon juice

1 1/2 tsps fine grain sea salt

1 tbsp freshly chopped basil or 1 1/2 tsp dried basil

1/2 tsp onion powder

1/8 tbsp of fresh chopped oregano or 1/8 tsp dried oregano

Nutrition Facts		
Serving Size 7oz (196g)		
Servings Per Container 4		
Amount Per Serving		
Calories 60	Calories from Fat 5	
		% Daily Value*
Total Fat 0g		0%
Saturated Fat 0g		0%
Trans Fat 0g		
Cholesterol 0mg		0%
Sodium 940mg		39%
Total Carbohydrate 14g		5%
Dietary Fiber 4g		16%
Sugars 6g		
Protein 2g		
Vitamin A 330%	•	Vitamin C 20%
Calcium 6%	•	Iron 6%

*Percent Daily Values are based on a 2,000 calorie diet. Your daily values may be higher or lower depending on your calorie needs.

	Calories:	2,000	2,500
Total Fat	Less than	65g	80g
Saturated Fat	Less than	20g	25g
Cholesterol	Less than	300mg	300mg
Sodium	Less than	2,400mg	2,400mg
Total Carbohydrate		300g	375g
Dietary Fiber		25g	30g

Calories per gram:
Fat 9 • Carbohydrate 4 • Protein 4

Heat a saucepan with 2 inches of water over medium heat; line with a steamer basket. Add carrot and beet, cover and steam until tender, about 10-15 minutes. Remove from the heat and set aside.

Meanwhile, heat the oil in a skillet over medium heat. Add onion; sauté for about 5 minutes until translucent. Add garlic; sauté for an additional 2 minutes, to brown.

Add carrot, beet, onion, garlic, lemon juice, sea salt, black pepper, basil, onion powder and oregano. Blend until fully incorporated. Return to skillet to medium-low heat to heat through.

Tips
A great substitution to Tomato Sauce.

Make this sauce the day before to infuse more flavoring.

This sauce is great to make extra and freeze in food saver bags or a mason jar; allowing 1" space at the top), then sealed in boiling water.

Servings: 6

Target source of Vitamin A, Vitamin C, Vitamin B6, Vitamin K, Dietary Fiber

SPICY GINGER SAUCE

2 tbsps creamy almond butter

1/2 cup water

1 tbsp tahini sauce

1 tsp sesame oil

1 tbsp Pickled Ginger, page 236

1 tsp chopped fresh ginger

1 minced garlic cloves

2-3 tsps coconut amino

1 tsp freshly squeezed lemon juice

2 tsps maple syrup, grade B

5 dashes organic cayenne, optional

1/8 tsp fine grain sea salt

1/8 tsp ground black pepper, to taste

Nutrition Facts

Serving Size 2oz (58g)
Servings Per Container 4

Amount Per Serving

Calories 100	Calories from Fat 70

	% Daily Value*
Total Fat 8g	12%
Saturated Fat 1g	5%
Trans Fat 0g	
Cholesterol 0mg	0%
Sodium 125mg	5%
Total Carbohydrate 6g	2%
Dietary Fiber 1g	4%
Sugars 3g	
Protein 3g	

Vitamin A 0%	•	Vitamin C 2%
Calcium 4%	•	Iron 2%

*Percent Daily Values are based on a 2,000 calorie diet. Your daily values may be higher or lower depending on your calorie needs.

	Calories	2,000	2,500
Total Fat	Less than	65g	80g
Saturated Fat	Less than	20g	25g
Cholesterol	Less than	300mg	300mg
Sodium	Less than	2,400mg	2,400mg
Total Carbohydrate		300g	375g
Dietary Fiber		25g	30g

Calories per gram:
Fat 9 • Carbohydrate 4 • Protein 4

Prepare Pickled Ginger.

Combine all ingredients into a small bowl; mix well. Transfer to a skillet and warm on medium-low heat; stirring frequently.

Allow all ingredients to incorporate. Transfer the sauce back into a serving bowl and cover to retain heat.

Servings: 4

267.

THE BEST PESTO

2 cups fresh basil leaves, with stem

2 cups fresh organic spinach leaves, with stem

2 chopped garlic clove

1/4 tsp fine sea salt, to taste

1/2 ground black pepper

1 cup extra virgin olive oil

2 tbsps pine nuts

Nutrition Facts
Serving Size 3 tbsp (51g)
Servings Per Container 8

Amount Per Serving

Calories 270   Calories from Fat 260

% Daily Value*

Total Fat 30g — 46%

Saturated Fat 4.5g — 23%

Trans Fat 0g

Cholesterol 0mg — 0%

Sodium 150mg — 6%

Total Carbohydrate 1g — 0%

Dietary Fiber 1g — 4%

Sugars 0g

Protein 1g

Vitamin A 25%   •   Vitamin C 8%

Calcium 2%   •   Iron 4%

*Percent Daily Values are based on a 2,000 calorie diet. Your daily values may be higher or lower depending on your calorie needs.

	Calories:	2,000	2,500
Total Fat	Less than	65g	80g
Saturated Fat	Less than	20g	25g
Cholesterol	Less than	300mg	300mg
Sodium	Less than	2,400mg	2,400mg
Total Carbohydrate		300g	375g
Dietary Fiber		25g	30g

Calories per gram:
Fat 9 • Carbohydrate 4 • Protein 4

In a food processor or blender, add basil, spinach, garlic, sea salt and ground black pepper; pulse until finely chopped. Turn processor to the "on" position; add oil in a slow stream to help emulsify. Turn off, and scrape down the sides as needed. Add pine nuts and pulse 5 times; rough chop.

Tips
Pesto is power packed and a great addition to your morning.

Make and freeze for later.

If you grow your own basil, pick it in the morning and stick the stems into water.

Yield: 3 to 3 1/2 cups

Target source of Vitamin A, Vitamin K, Manganese, Dietary Fats

TACO SAUCE

1 cup Basic Tomato Sauce, page 250

2/3 cup organic vegetable broth

2 tbsps white vinegar

1 tbsp ground cumin

2 tsps onion powder

1 tsp garlic powder

1 tsp garlic salt

1/2 tsp organic chili powder

1/2 tsp ground paprika

1/2 tsp coconut sugar

1/2 tsp organic cayenne

Nutrition Facts

Serving Size 1/2 cup (115g)
Servings Per Container 4

Amount Per Serving

Calories 60	Calories from Fat 25

	% Daily Value*
Total Fat 2.5g	4%
Saturated Fat 0g	0%
Trans Fat 0g	
Cholesterol 0mg	0%
Sodium 690mg	29%
Total Carbohydrate 9g	3%
Dietary Fiber 2g	8%
Sugars 5g	
Protein 2g	

Vitamin A 10%	•	Vitamin C 2%
Calcium 2%	•	Iron 6%

*Percent Daily Values are based on a 2,000 calorie diet. Your daily values may be higher or lower depending on your calorie needs.

	Calories	2,000	2,500
Total Fat	Less than	65g	80g
Saturated Fat	Less than	20g	25g
Cholesterol	Less than	300mg	300mg
Sodium	Less than	2,400mg	2,400mg
Total Carbohydrate		300g	375g
Dietary Fiber		25g	30g

Calories per gram:
Fat 9 • Carbohydrate 4 • Protein 4

Prepare Tomato Sauce.

Combine tomato sauce, broth, vinegar, cumin, onion powder, garlic powder, garlic salt, chili powder, paprika, sugar, and cayenne together in a saucepan over medium-low heat; simmer until slightly thickened, about 20 minutes. Cool sauce slightly before serving.

Servings: 4

TZATZIKI SAUCE

1 1/2 cups Sour Cream, page 239

1/4 cup small diced organic cucumber

2 tbsps dill weed

Prepare Sour Cream.

Combine sour cream, cucumbers and dill weed in a small bowl; mix well. Cover and refrigerate for 1 hour to infuse the flavors.

Yield: 1 1/2 cups

Nutrition Facts

Serving Size 1/4 cup (40g)
Servings Per Container 10

Amount Per Serving

Calories 160   Calories from Fat 160

	% Daily Value*
Total Fat 18g	28%
Saturated Fat 10g	50%
Trans Fat 0g	
Cholesterol 20mg	7%
Sodium 15mg	1%
Total Carbohydrate 2g	1%
Dietary Fiber 0g	0%
Sugars 0g	
Protein 1g	

Vitamin A 2%	•	Vitamin C 2%	
Calcium 2%	•	Iron 6%	

*Percent Daily Values are based on a 2,000 calorie diet. Your daily values may be higher or lower depending on your calorie needs.

	Calories	2,000	2,500
Total Fat	Less than	65g	80g
Saturated Fat	Less than	20g	25g
Cholesterol	Less than	300mg	300mg
Sodium	Less than	2,400mg	2,400mg
Total Carbohydrate		300g	375g
Dietary Fiber		25g	30g

Calories per gram
Fat 9 • Carbohydrate 4 • Protein 4

SIDE DISH /
APPETIZER

ACORN SQUASH WITH PEAR STUFFING

2 tbsps Clarified Butter, page 203

2 acorn squash

1 1/2 cups chopped sweet onion

3 chopped organic pears, peeled and cored

2 tbsps coconut sugar

1 tsp fine grain sea salt

1/2 tsp ground black pepper

3/4 tsp grated fresh ginger root

1/2 tsp grated fresh nutmeg

Nutrition Facts

Serving Size 1 (416g)
Servings Per Container 4

Amount Per Serving

Calories 270   Calories from Fat 70

% Daily Value*

Total Fat 7g	11%
Saturated Fat 4.5g	23%
Trans Fat 0g	
Cholesterol 20mg	7%
Sodium 500mg	21%
Total Carbohydrate 52g	17%
Dietary Fiber 7g	28%
Sugars 21g	
Protein 3g	

Vitamin A 20%	•	Vitamin C 60%	
Calcium 10%	•	Iron 45%	

*Percent Daily Values are based on a 2,000 calorie diet. Your daily values may be higher or lower depending on your calorie needs.

		Calories	2,000	2,800
Total Fat	Less than		65g	80g
Saturated Fat	Less than		20g	25g
Cholesterol	Less than		300mg	300mg
Sodium	Less than		2,400mg	2,400mg
Total Carbohydrate			300g	375g
Dietary Fiber			25g	30g

Calories per gram
Fat 9 • Carbohydrate 4 • Protein 4

Preheat oven to 400° F.

Prepare Clarified Butter.

Cut the bottom end off the acorn squash so that you have a stable base for cutting in half, lengthwise; discard seed and membrane. Place each half in a sheet pan, open side down; add 1 inch of water. Bake uncovered for 30 minutes.

Filling: Melt clarified butter in large skillet over med heat. Add the onion; sauté for 5 minutes until translucent. Add the onion, pear, coconut sugar, sea salt, black pepper, ginger-root and nutmeg; sauté for 5 minutes, stirring occasionally.

Remove squash from oven and drain the remaining water. Turn acorn squash open side up and set aside. Reduce the oven temperature to 350° F. Fill the acorn squash halves using a spoon. Return the acorn squash to the oven for 5-10 minutes, uncovered.

Servings: 4

Target source of Zinc, Vitamin C, Iron, Manganese, Dietary Fiber

Supportive of Immune and Gut Health

APPLE STUFFED MUSHROOMS

8 large Portobello mushroom caps; reserve mushroom stems

2 tbsps extra virgin olive oil

1/2 cup diced mushroom stems

1/4 cup chopped onion

1 minced garlic clove

1/4 cup almond meal

1 chopped organic Granny Smith apple

1/4 tsp fine grain sea salt

1/2 tsp ground black pepper

3 tbsps finely chopped pecan

1/2 tbsp extra virgin olive oil

Nutrition Facts
Serving Size 1 (138g)
Servings Per Container 8

Amount Per Serving

Calories 110   Calories from Fat 80

% Daily Value*

Total Fat 9g — 14%
  Saturated Fat 2g — 10%
  Trans Fat 0g
Cholesterol 0mg — 0%
Sodium 100mg — 4%
Total Carbohydrate 7g — 2%
  Dietary Fiber 2g — 8%
  Sugars 4g
Protein 3g

Vitamin A 0% • Vitamin C 2%
Calcium 2% • Iron 4%

*Percent Daily Values are based on a 2,000 calorie diet. Your daily values may be higher or lower depending on your calorie needs.

	Calories	2,000	2,500
Total Fat	Less than	65g	80g
Saturated Fat	Less than	20g	25g
Cholesterol	Less than	300mg	300mg
Sodium	Less than	2,400mg	2,400mg
Total Carbohydrate		300g	375g
Dietary Fiber		25g	30g

Calories per gram
Fat 9 • Carbohydrate 4 • Protein 4

Wash the mushroom caps and remove gills. Remove stems, dice and set mushrooms and stems aside, separately.

Filling: Heat 2 tablespoons of oil in a skillet over medium heat. Add mushroom stems, onion, and garlic; sauté 3-5 minutes. Remove the skillet from the heat. Stir in almond meal, apple, sea salt and black pepper. Spoon the filling into the caps. Place on a lightly sprayed sheet pan.

Combine pecans with 1 tablespoon of oil and sprinkle over caps. Bake in the oven 350° F for 15-17 minutes until heated through. Turn the oven to broil and cook 1-2 minutes, until slightly browned.

Servings: 8

Target source of Vitamin B3 (niacin), Copper, Selenium, Dietary Fiber

Supportive of Immune, Heart and Gut Health

275.

APRICOT, CURRY AND MUSTARD CARROTS

1 lb organic carrots, peeled and cut into 1/2-inch slices

2 tsps Clarified Butter, page 203

1 tsp extra virgin olive oil

1 tbsp organic apricot preserve

1 1/2 tsps freshly squeezed lemon juice

3/4 tsp Dijon Mustard, page 228

1 tsp curry powder

1 1/2 tsps coconut sugar

1/4 cup organic dried dark raisin

Nutrition Facts	
Serving Size 5 oz (138g)	
Servings Per Container 4	
Amount Per Serving	
Calories 120	Calories from Fat 35
	% Daily Value*
Total Fat 4g	6%
Saturated Fat 1g	5%
Trans Fat 0g	
Cholesterol 5mg	2%
Sodium 95mg	4%
Total Carbohydrate 22g	7%
Dietary Fiber 4g	16%
Sugars 15g	
Protein 1g	
Vitamin A 380% • Vitamin C 15%	
Calcium 6% • Iron 4%	

*Percent Daily Values are based on a 2,000 calorie diet. Your daily values may be higher or lower depending on your calorie needs.

	Calories:	2,000	2,500
Total Fat	Less than	65g	80g
Saturated Fat	Less than	20g	25g
Cholesterol	Less than	300mg	300mg
Sodium	Less than	2,400mg	2,400mg
Total Carbohydrate		300g	375g
Dietary Fiber		25g	30g

Calories per gram:
Fat 9 • Carbohydrate 4 • Protein 4

Prepare Clarified Butter and Dijon Mustard.

Bring water to a boil in a medium saucepan over high heat, lined with a steam basket. Place carrots in the basket and cover; steam for 5-7 minutes or until almost tender. Carefully remove steamer basket from the saucepan.

Heat the clarified butter and oil in a large skillet over medium high heat. When hot, cook the carrot for 1 minute. Stir in coconut sugar and raisin; sauté for 1-2 minutes.

In a mixing bowl, combine organic apricot preserves, lemon juice, Dijon mustard, and curry powder; mix well. Add preserve mixture to the saucepan; sauté for 2-3 minutes until carrots are glazed, stirring often. Scrape down the sides of the skillet, as needed.

Servings: 4

Target source of Vitamin A, Vitamin K, B Vitamins, Magnesium, Potassium, Zinc, Dietary Fiber

Supportive of Immune, Detoxification and Gut Health

ARTICHOKES WITH LEMON BUTTER

2 large artichokes

2 freshly squeezed lemon juice

2 tbsps whole coriander seed

1 tbsp fine grain sea salt

1 cup melted Clarified Butter, page 203

Nutrition Facts
Serving Size 1 artichoke (340g)
Servings Per Container 2

Amount Per Serving

Calories 1150 Calories from Fat 1020

	% Daily Value*
Total Fat 113g	174%
Saturated Fat 72g	360%
Trans Fat 0g	
Cholesterol 320mg	107%
Sodium 1310mg	55%
Total Carbohydrate 25g	8%
Dietary Fiber 13g	52%
Sugars 4g	
Protein 6g	

Vitamin A 80%	•	Vitamin C 70%	
Calcium 15%	•	Iron 15%	

*Percent Daily Values are based on a 2,000 calorie diet. Your daily values may be higher or lower depending on your calorie needs

	Calories	2,000	2,500
Total Fat	Less than	65g	80g
Saturated Fat	Less than	20g	25g
Cholesterol	Less than	300mg	300mg
Sodium	Less than	2,400mg	2,400mg
Total Carbohydrate		300g	375g
Dietary Fiber		25g	30g

Calories per gram
Fat 9 • Carbohydrate 4 • Protein 4

Prepare Clarified Butter.

Wash artichokes under cold running water. Cut off stems at base and remove small bottom leaves. Heat 5 quarts of water in a saucepan over high heat, with the juice of 3 lemon halves. Add squeezed lemons, coriander seeds, sea salt and water; boil for 5 minutes.

Place artichokes in water and cover with heavy object to prevent artichokes from floating. Boil for approximately 15 minutes or until a knife can insert easily where stems meets the bottom. Meanwhile, melt clarified butter and juice of remaining lemons.

Serve with butter sauce on the side. Pull each leaf off and dip in butter sauce. The attachment end of the leaves is where the meat is, scrap with teeth.

Servings: 2

Target source of Dietary Fiber, Vitamin C, Vitamin K, Vitamins B1, B2, B3, B6, Folate, Calcium, Copper, Iron, Magnesium, Manganese, Phosphorus, Potassium, Zinc

Supportive of Immune and Detoxification Health

AVOCADO DEVILED EGGS

9 free-range eggs, boiled and cut in half; yolk reserved

1 avocado, peeled and seeded

1 tsp freshly squeezed lemon juice; to prevent browning

3 slices uncured crumbled bacon; reserve 1 tbsp bacon fat

1/4 tsp ground paprika

1/8 tsp fine grain sea salt, more if desired

Nutrition Facts

Serving Size 1 egg (190g)
Servings Per Container 9

Amount Per Serving

Calories 260	Calories from Fat 190

	% Daily Value*
Total Fat 21g	32%
Saturated Fat 4.5g	23%
Trans Fat 0g	
Cholesterol 220mg	73%
Sodium 160mg	7%
Total Carbohydrate 12g	4%
Dietary Fiber 7g	28%
Sugars 4g	
Protein 10g	

Vitamin A 10%	•	Vitamin C 40%
Calcium 4%	•	Iron 6%

*Percent Daily Values are based on a 2,000 calorie diet. Your daily values may be higher or lower depending on your calorie needs.

		Calories:	2,000	2,500
Total Fat	Less than		65g	80g
Saturated Fat	Less than		20g	25g
Cholesterol	Less than		300mg	300mg
Sodium	Less than		2,400mg	2,400mg
Total Carbohydrate			300g	375g
Dietary Fiber			25g	30g

Calories per gram:
Fat 9 • Carbohydrate 4 • Protein 4

Bring water to a boil in a large saucepan over high heat. Boil for 15 minutes, strain and cool in cold water. Remove shell and cut each egg in half; reserve half of the yolks in a separate bowl. Wash egg halves and turn upside down on paper towel to air dry.

Heat a skillet over medium-high heat; add bacon until crisp. Place the bacon on a paper towel to drain; reserve 1 tablespoon of bacon fat. Crumble bacon into small pieces and set aside.

Combine the avocado, half of the egg yolks together, half of the crumbled bacon, reserved bacon fat and lemon juice; mash to incorporate. You want a smooth consistency.

Take a piping bag or a zip lock bag; cutting a 1/4-inch off the bottom corner. Fill the bag with the avocado mixture. Sprinkle with paprika and remaining crumbled bacon.

Yield: 9

Target source of Protein, Dietary Fiber, Dietary Fats, Vitamin A, Vitamin C, Vitamin B12, other B Vitamins, Folate, Pantothenic Acid, Copper, Potassium

Supportive of Immune, Detoxification and Gut Health

BACON BRAISED BRUSSELS SPROUTS

4 bacon slices, cook and crumble
Water
16 each Brussels sprouts

Nutrition Facts
Serving Size 4 each (90g)
Servings Per Container 4

Amount Per Serving

Calories 60 Calories from Fat 20

% Daily Value*

Total Fat 2g	3%
Saturated Fat 0.5g	3%
Trans Fat 0g	
Cholesterol 5mg	2%
Sodium 115mg	5%
Total Carbohydrate 6g	2%
Dietary Fiber 3g	12%
Sugars 1g	
Protein 4g	

| Vitamin A 15% | • | Vitamin C 90% |
| Calcium 4% | • | Iron 6% |

*Percent Daily Values are based on a 2,000 calorie diet. Your daily values may be higher or lower depending on your calorie needs.

	Calories	2,000	2,500
Total Fat	Less than	65g	80g
Saturated Fat	Less than	20g	25g
Cholesterol	Less than	300mg	300mg
Sodium	Less than	2,400mg	2,400mg
Total Carbohydrate		300g	375g
Dietary Fiber		25g	30g

Calories per gram:
Fat 9 • Carbohydrate 4 • Protein 4

Prepare ice bath for blanching. Fill up a bowl of ice with water.

Wash Brussels sprouts, sprinkle with a little sea salt and let strain; sea salt helps sprouts sweat their natural water.

Cook bacon, about 5-7 minutes until crispy; reserve bacon fat. Let bacon cool and crumble or cut into smaller pieces. Brussels sprouts. Heat the water to boiling water over high heat. Dip the entire strainer into boiling water for 30-45 seconds; blanch in two batches, if necessary.

Blanch Brussels sprouts. Heat the water to boiling water over high heat. Dip the entire strainer into boiling water for 30-45 seconds; blanch in two batches, if necessary.

The green chlorophyll will brighten. Immediately transfer strainer to ice bath to stop the cooking process. Remove from ice water and let strain.

Heat up the reserved bacon fat on medium-high heat. Add Brussels sprouts, cover and sauté for 7-10 minutes, to soften and heat throughout.

Toss with crumbled bacon and serve.

Servings: 4

Target source of Vitamin K, Folate, Iron, Dietary Fats, Dietary Fiber, Vitamin C, Vitamin A, Manganese

Supportive of Detoxification and Gut Health

BRAISED GREEN CABBAGE

1 head chopped cabbage

1 cup organic beef broth or organic vegetable broth

1/4 cup chopped onion

2 tbsps extra virgin olive oil

1 tsp fine grain sea salt

1/4 tsp ground pepper

Nutrition Facts

Serving Size 7oz (193g)
Servings Per Container 8

Amount Per Serving

Calories 40   Calories from Fat 0

% Daily Value*

Total Fat 0g	0%
Saturated Fat 0g	0%
Trans Fat 0g	
Cholesterol 0mg	0%
Sodium 390mg	16%
Total Carbohydrate 9g	3%
Dietary Fiber 3g	12%
Sugars 5g	
Protein 2g	

Vitamin A 2% • Vitamin C 100%

Calcium 8% • Iron 2%

*Percent Daily Values are based on a 2,000 calorie diet. Your daily values may be higher or lower depending on your calorie needs.

		Calories	2,000	2,500
Total Fat	Less than		65g	80g
Saturated Fat	Less than		20g	25g
Cholesterol	Less than		300mg	300mg
Sodium	Less than		2,400mg	2,400mg
Total Carbohydrate			300g	375g
Dietary Fiber			25g	30g

Calories per gram:
Fat 9 • Carbohydrate 4 • Protein 4

Heat the oil in a skillet over medium-high heat. Add cabbage, beef broth and onion; sauté until cabbage has begun to soften. Drain broth and sprinkle with sea salt and black, pepper to taste.

Servings: 8

Target source of Dietary Fiber, Vitamin C, Folate, Vitamin K, Manganese, Vitamin B6

Supportive of Immune, Detoxification and Gut Health

BREADED ZUCCHINI BITES

3 sliced zucchini

1 cup almond meal

2 free-range eggs, beaten

1/4 cup coconut milk

2 tbsps extra virgin olive oil

Nutrition Facts

Serving Size 7oz (218g)
Servings Per Container 4

Amount Per Serving	
Calories 280	Calories from Fat 210

	% Daily Value^
Total Fat 23g	**35%**
Saturated Fat 5g	**25%**
Trans Fat 0g	
Cholesterol 110mg	**37%**
Sodium 55mg	**2%**
Total Carbohydrate 11g	**4%**
Dietary Fiber 4g	**16%**
Sugars 5g	
Protein 11g	

Vitamin A 8%	•	Vitamin C 45%
Calcium 10%	•	Iron 15%

*Percent Daily Values are based on a 2,000 calorie diet. Your daily values may be higher or lower depending on your calorie needs.

	Calories	2,000	2,500
Total Fat	Less than	65g	80g
Saturated Fat	Less than	20g	25g
Cholesterol	Less than	300mg	300mg
Sodium	Less than	2,400mg	2,400mg
Total Carbohydrate		300g	375g
Dietary Fiber		25g	30g

Calories per gram
Fat 9 • Carbohydrate 4 • Protein 4

Preheat oven to 400° F.

Slice zucchini and blanch. Heat the water to boiling water over high heat. Dip the entire strainer into boiling water for 30-45 seconds; blanch in two batches, if they cannot be fully dipped. The green chlorophyll will brighten. Immediately transfer strainer to ice bath to stop the cooking process. Remove from ice water and let strain.

Prepare egg and milk mixture and bowl of almond meal. Dip zucchini in egg/milk mixture, and then dredge through almond flour. Place on a sheet pan sprayed with cooking spray.

Drizzle extra oil on top of zucchini, if you prefer. Bake for 20 minutes.

Servings: 4

Target source of Protein, Dietary Fats, Dietary Fiber, B Vitamins, Vitamin C, Iron, Magnesium, Potassium, Calcium, Molybdenum, Manganese

Supportive of Immune and Gut Health

CANADIAN BACON AND TOMATO POTATO SKINS STRIPS

6 organic Yukon gold potatoes

2 tsps extra virgin olive oil

1 tsp organic chili powder

1 tsp chipotle Tabasco sauce

2/3 cup uncured, pastured Canadian bacon

1 cup finely chopped organic tomato, seeded and juiced

2 tbsps finely chopped green onion

3/4 cup Sour Cream, page 239

3/4 cup Guacamole, page 230

Nutrition Facts

Serving Size 10 oz (304g)
Servings Per Container 6

Amount Per Serving

Calories 360	Calories from Fat 180

	% Daily Value*
Total Fat 21g	**32%**
Saturated Fat 10g	**50%**
Trans Fat 0g	
Cholesterol 30mg	**10%**
Sodium 320mg	**13%**
Total Carbohydrate 37g	**12%**
Dietary Fiber 4g	**16%**
Sugars 4g	
Protein 9g	

Vitamin A 5%	•	Vitamin C 40%
Calcium 4%	•	Iron 15%

*Percent Daily Values are based on a 2,000 calorie diet. Your daily values may be higher or lower depending on your calorie needs.

	Calories	2,000	2,500
Total Fat	Less than	65g	80g
Saturated Fat	Less than	20g	25g
Cholesterol	Less than	300mg	300mg
Sodium	Less than	2,400mg	2,400mg
Total Carbohydrate		300g	375g
Dietary Fiber		25g	30g

Calories per gram:
Fat 9 • Carbohydrate 4 • Protein 4

Preheat oven to 425° F.

Prepare Sour Cream and Guacamole.

Scrub and wash gold potatoes, leaving skin. Wrap with aluminum foil and poke with a fork.

Bake for 35-40 minutes until tender. Let cool and cut lengthwise, in half. Scoop out the inside of each potato half, leaving about a 1/4-inch thick shell. Place the open side down on lightly sprayed sheet pan. Set aside to cool. Turn oven heat to 450° F.

Combine the cooking oil, chili powder and Tabasco sauce. Brush the outside potato skin with oil mixture. Cut the potato bowls into three strips. Sprinkle potato strips with
Canadian bacon, tomato and green onion.

Bake at 450° F for 10 to 12 minutes until potato strips are heated through. Transfer to the plate with a spatula. Serve with a dollop sour cream or guacamole, if desired.

Tip
Reserve the inside mashed potato or freeze for later.

Servings: 6

Target source of *Protein, Dietary Fiber, Dietary Fat, Vitamins B1, B3, B6, Vitamin C, Folate, Manganese, Potassium, Phosphorus, Copper, Iron, Magnesium, Zinc*

Supportive of Immune, Detoxification and Gut Health

CAULIFLOWER RICE

1 grated cauliflower head

2 tbsps Clarified Butter, page 203

1/8 tsp fine grain sea salt, to taste

1/8 tsp black pepper, to taste

Nutrition Facts
Serving Size (217g)
Servings Per Container

Amount Per Serving

Calories 120   Calories from Fat 70

% Daily Value*

Total Fat 8g	12%
Saturated Fat 5g	25%
Trans Fat 0g	
Cholesterol 20mg	7%
Sodium 65mg	3%
Total Carbohydrate 10g	3%
Dietary Fiber 4g	16%
Sugars 4g	
Protein 4g	

Vitamin A 6%	•	Vitamin C 170%
Calcium 4%	•	Iron 4%

*Percent Daily Values are based on a 2,000 calorie diet. Your daily values may be higher or lower depending on your calorie needs

		Calories	2,000	2,500
Total Fat	Less than		65g	80g
Saturated Fat	Less than		20g	25g
Cholesterol	Less than		300mg	300mg
Sodium	Less than		2,400mg	2,400mg
Total Carbohydrate			300g	375g
Dietary Fiber			25g	30g

Calories per gram
Fat 9 • Carbohydrate 4 • Protein 4

Prepare Clarified Butter.

Grate fresh cauliflower to resemble "rice". Heat clarified butter in a skillet over medium heat, sauté cauliflower with sea salt and black pepper for 2-3 minutes, stirring occasionally.

Servings: 4

Target source of Vitamin C, Vitamin K, Folate, Dietary Fiber

Supportive of Detoxification Health and Gut Flora Balance

CAULIFLOWER RICE PILAF

2 tbsps extra virgin olive oil

1 finely chopped organic celery stalk

1 finely chopped organic carrot, peeled

3 1/2 cups grated cauliflower

1/2 tsp fine sea salt

1/2 tsp ground black pepper

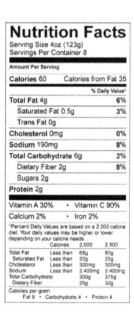

Nutrition Facts
Serving Size 4oz (123g)
Servings Per Container 8

Amount Per Serving

Calories 60   Calories from Fat 35

% Daily Value*

Total Fat 4g	6%
Saturated Fat 0.5g	3%
Trans Fat 0g	
Cholesterol 0mg	0%
Sodium 190mg	8%
Total Carbohydrate 6g	2%
Dietary Fiber 2g	8%
Sugars 2g	
Protein 2g	

Vitamin A 30%	•	Vitamin C 90%
Calcium 2%	•	Iron 2%

*Percent Daily Values are based on a 2,000 calorie diet. Your daily values may be higher or lower depending on your calorie needs.

		Calories:	2,000	2,800
Total Fat	Less than		65g	60g
Saturated Fat	Less than		20g	25g
Cholesterol	Less than		300mg	300mg
Sodium	Less than		2,400mg	2,400mg
Total Carbohydrate			300g	375g
Dietary Fiber			25g	30g

Calories per gram:
Fat 9 • Carbohydrate 4 • Protein 4

Preheat oven to 450° F.

Grate fresh cauliflower, until it is the size of rice.

Heat the oil in a medium skillet over medium-high heat. Add carrot and celery; sauté for 2 minutes until slightly tender. Add grated cauliflower and toss to coat; sauté for about 2 minute heat through.

To roast cauliflower. Add cauliflower rice to a sheet pan sprayed with cooking oil. Place in the oven up to 10 minutes until cooked through, about 5-7 minutes.

Servings: 8

Target source of Dietary Fiber, Vitamin B6, Folate, Vitamin C, Vitamin K, Potassium

Supportive of Immune, Detoxification and Gut Health

COCONUT CREAMED POTATOES AND PLUM TOMATOES

3 lbs sliced organic Yukon potato, peeled

1 1/2 cups coconut milk

1 cup coconut milk, full fat (in a can)

4 thinly sliced chive

2 chopped organic plum tomatoes, seeded

1/4 tsp fine grain sea salt

1/4 tsp freshly ground white pepper

Nutrition Facts

Serving Size 5 oz (131g)
Servings Per Container 16

Amount Per Serving

Calories 150	Calories from Fat 60

	% Daily Value^
Total Fat 7g	11%
Saturated Fat 3.5g	18%
Trans Fat 0g	
Cholesterol 0mg	0%
Sodium 330mg	14%
Total Carbohydrate 19g	6%
Dietary Fiber 2g	8%
Sugars 1g	
Protein 2g	

Vitamin A 4%	•	Vitamin C 6%
Calcium 6%	•	Iron 8%

*Percent Daily Values are based on a 2,000 calorie diet. Your daily values may be higher or lower depending on your calorie needs.

	Calories	2,000	2,500
Total Fat	Less than	65g	80g
Saturated Fat	Less than	20g	25g
Cholesterol	Less than	300mg	300mg
Sodium	Less than	2,400mg	2,400mg
Total Carbohydrate		300g	375g
Dietary Fiber		25g	30g

Calories per gram:
Fat 9 • Carbohydrate 4 • Protein 4

Preheat the oven to 350° F.

Scrub and peel potato. Wrap the potato in aluminum foil; bake for about 1 hour until tender.

Heat a large saucepan over medium-low heat. Add coconut milk and coconut milk full fat.

Cut the potato in half and scoop out the inside into the saucepan; mash until incorporated an creamy.. Stir in the chive, plum tomato, sea salt and white pepper; sauté for 3-5 minutes.

Tip
If you pre-make this recipe, leave out the plum tomatoes and chives unil after you have preheated the potato.

Servings: 16

Target source of Chromium, Iron, Dietary Fats

CREAMED PEARL ONIONS

3 cups pearled onion

1 cup coconut milk, full fat (in a can)

2 bay leaves

1 tbsp chopped parsley

1 crushed garlic clove

1/2 tsp grated fresh nutmeg

1/4 tsp fine grain sea salt

1/4 tsp ground black pepper

1 cup organic chicken stock

Nutrition Facts		
Serving Size 1/2 cup (136g)		
Servings Per Container 6		
Amount Per Serving		
Calories 110	Calories from Fat 70	
		% Daily Value*
Total Fat 8g		12%
Saturated Fat 7g		35%
Trans Fat 0g		
Cholesterol 0mg		0%
Sodium 135mg		6%
Total Carbohydrate 10g		3%
Dietary Fiber 0g		0%
Sugars 2g		
Protein 2g		
Vitamin A 2%	•	Vitamin C 6%
Calcium 2%	•	Iron 8%

*Percent Daily Values are based on a 2,000 calorie diet. Your daily values may be higher or lower depending on your calorie needs.

	Calories	2,000	2,500
Total Fat	Less than	65g	80g
Saturated Fat	Less than	20g	25g
Cholesterol	Less than	300mg	300mg
Sodium	Less than	2,400mg	2,400mg
Total Carbohydrate		300g	375g
Dietary Fiber		25g	30g

Calories per gram:
Fat 9 • Carbohydrate 4 • Protein 4

Prepare an ice bath, with water and ice in a bowl.

Heat water in a saucepan over high heat; bring to a boil. Add pearl onions and boil for about 10 minute. Remove pearl onion and drop in the ice bath, to stop the cooking process; drain. Cut off one end and remove the skin.

Heat the same saucepan over medium-low heat. Add full fat coconut milk, bay leaves, parsley, garlic, nutmeg, sea salt and black pepper.

Cover and simmer for 10 minutes, stirring occasionally. Once sauce thickens, uncover and add chicken stock; season to taste. Let the saucepan sit for 5 minutes to thicken cream sauce. Discard the bay leaves before serving.

Servings: 6

Target source of Dietary Fiber, Dietary Fats, Vitamin K, Iron, Manganese

Supportive of Immune and Detoxification Health

293.

GARLIC GREEN BEANS

1 tbsp Clarified Butter, page 203

1 minced garlic clove

1 1/2 lbs fresh green beans, trimmed

1/8 tsp fine grain sea salt

1/8 tsp ground black pepper

Nutrition Facts		
Serving Size 4 1/2 oz (130g)		
Servings Per Container 5		
Amount Per Serving		
Calories 140	Calories from Fat 100	
		% Daily Value*
Total Fat 11g		**17%**
Saturated Fat 3g		**15%**
Trans Fat 0g		
Cholesterol 10mg		**3%**
Sodium 10mg		**0%**
Total Carbohydrate 10g		**3%**
Dietary Fiber 3g		**12%**
Sugars 4g		
Protein 2g		
Vitamin A 20%	•	Vitamin C 25%
Calcium 6%	•	Iron 8%

*Percent Daily Values are based on a 2,000 calorie diet. Your daily values may be higher or lower depending on your calorie needs.

	Calories	2,000	2,500
Total Fat	Less than	65g	80g
Saturated Fat	Less than	20g	25g
Cholesterol	Less than	300mg	300mg
Sodium	Less than	2,400mg	2,400mg
Total Carbohydrate		300g	375g
Dietary Fiber		25g	30g

Calories per gram:
Fat 9 • Carbohydrate 4 • Protein 4

Prepare Clarified Butter.

Melt clarified butter with oil in a skillet over medium heat. Add garlic, and sauté until lightly browned, stirring frequently. Add green beans, sea salt and black pepper; sauté about 10 minutes until tender.

Servings: 4

Target source of Vitamin C, Dietary Fiber, Vitamin K, Manganese, Dietary Fats

Supportive of Detoxification and Gut Health

GARLIC INFUSED ARTICHOKES

1 1/2 lbs organic artichoke heart

2 minced garlic clove

1/2 cup coarsely chopped shallot

2 tbsps extra virgin olive oil

2 tbsps chopped fresh parsley

Nutrition Facts

Serving Size 3/4 cup (200g)

Servings Per Container 4

Amount Per Serving

Calories 140   Calories from Fat 60

	% Daily Value*
Total Fat 7g	11%
Saturated Fat 1g	5%
Trans Fat 0g	
Cholesterol 0mg	0%
Sodium 500mg	21%
Total Carbohydrate 16g	5%
Dietary Fiber 3g	12%
Sugars 4g	
Protein 5g	

Vitamin A 8%	•	Vitamin C 20%	
Calcium 6%	•	Iron 15%	

*Percent Daily Values are based on a 2,000 calorie diet. Your daily values may be higher or lower depending on your calorie needs.

		Calories	2,000	2,500
Total Fat	Less than		65g	80g
Saturated Fat	Less than		20g	25g
Cholesterol	Less than		300mg	300mg
Sodium	Less than		2,400mg	2,400mg
Total Carbohydrate			300g	375g
Dietary Fiber			25g	30g

Calories per gram:

Fat 9 • Carbohydrate 4 • Protein 4

Heat the oil in a skillet over medium-high heat. Add artichoke heart, garlic and shallot. Cover and sauté for about 3-5 minutes; stirring frequently.

Heat the oil in a skillet over medium-high heat. Add artichoke heart, garlic and shallot. Cover and sauté for about 3-5 minutes; stirring frequently.

Add sea salt and black pepper. Sauté an additional 5 minutes until liquid has evaporated and artichokes are tender. Garnish with parsley.

Servings: 4

Target source of Dietary Fiber, Dietary Fats, Vitamin A, Vitamin C, Vitamin K, Iron

Supportive of Immune Health

296.

GOURMET MUSHROOMS

4 oz sliced large Portobello mushroom caps; gill and stem
   removed

1/4 cup roughly chopped shitake or oyster mushroom

1/4 cup thinly sliced button mushroom

3 tbsps extra virgin olive oil

3 minced garlic clove

1 tbsps minced organic sun-dried tomato

1/2 cup pine nut

2 tbsps parsley, garnish

Nutrition Facts

Serving Size 1/2 cup (103g)
Servings Per Container 6

Amount Per Serving

Calories 150	Calories from Fat 130

	% Daily Value*
Total Fat 14g	22%
Saturated Fat 1.5g	8%
Trans Fat 0g	
Cholesterol 0mg	0%
Sodium 10mg	0%
Total Carbohydrate 6g	2%
Dietary Fiber 2g	8%
Sugars 3g	
Protein 3g	

Vitamin A 2%	•	Vitamin C 4%
Calcium 0%	•	Iron 6%

*Percent Daily Values are based on a 2,000 calorie diet. Your daily values may be higher or lower depending on your calorie needs.

	Calories	2,000	2,500
Total Fat	Less than	65g	80g
Saturated Fat	Less than	20g	25g
Cholesterol	Less than	300mg	300mg
Sodium	Less than	2,400mg	2,400mg
Total Carbohydrate		300g	375g
Dietary Fiber		25g	30g

Calories per gram
Fat 9 • Carbohydrate 4 • Protein 4

Boil water or broth over high heat; add sundried tomato and remove from heat to allow sun-dried tomato to pop.

Wash and remove gill and stem from mushroom. Heat the oil in a skillet over medium heat. Add mushroom, garlic, sun-dried tomato and pine nut; sauté for 7-10 minutes until mushrooms are softened. Garnish with chopped parsley.

Servings: 6

Target source of Protein, Dietary Fiber, Dietary Fats, B Vitamins, Vitamin K, Pantothenic Acid, Copper, Phosphorus, Potassium, Selenium, Zinc

Supportive of Immune Health

297.

MUSHROOMS WITH MARSALA WINE

1 1/2 cups thinly sliced onion

1 cup thinly sliced organic red bell pepper

2 tbsps extra virgin olive oil

1/2 tsp fine grain sea salt

1/2 tsp ground black pepper

24 oz exotic mushroom blend (such as shitake, cremini, and oyster)

1 tbsps extra virgin olive oil

3 tbsps Marsala wine

Nutrition Facts

Serving Size 1/2 cup (130g)
Servings Per Container 8

Amount Per Serving

Calories 80	Calories from Fat 50

	% Daily Value*
Total Fat 6g	9%
Saturated Fat 1g	5%
Trans Fat 0g	
Cholesterol 0mg	0%
Sodium 190mg	8%
Total Carbohydrate 6g	2%
Dietary Fiber 1g	4%
Sugars 4g	
Protein 3g	

Vitamin A 8%	•	Vitamin C 30%
Calcium 0%	•	Iron 2%

*Percent Daily Values are based on a 2,000 calorie diet. Your daily values may be higher or lower depending on your calorie needs.

	Calories:	2,000	2,500
Total Fat	Less than	65g	80g
Saturated Fat	Less than	20g	25g
Cholesterol	Less than	300mg	300mg
Sodium	Less than	2,400mg	2,400mg
Total Carbohydrate		300g	375g
Dietary Fiber		25g	30g

Calories per gram:
Fat 9 • Carbohydrate 4 • Protein 4

Heat the oil in a skillet over medium-high heat. Add onion and bell pepper; sauté for 5 minutes until the onions begin to brown. Add salt, black pepper, exotic mushroom and oil to skillet; sauté 3 minutes or until mushrooms are tender and onion starts to caramelize.

Add Marsala wine; cook for 1 minute or until heated throughout.

Servings: 8

Target source of Vitamins B1, B2, B3, Biotin, Vitamin B6, Vitamin C, Pantothenic Acid, Copper, Phosphorus, Potassium, Selenium, Zinc

Supportive of Immune Health

NIGHTSHADE FREE POTATO SALAD

4 sweet potatoes, cut into 1/2-inch cubes

1 tsp fine grain sea salt

5 free-range eggs, soft boiled

3/4 cup chopped organic celery stalk, about 3

1/2 finely chopped shallot

1 small can organic unsweetened pineapple chunks

3/4 cup diced apple, peeled and cored

3/4 cup pecan pieces, Toasted Nuts, page 241

DRESSING

4 tbsps extra virgin olive oil

4 tbsps Dijon Mustard, page 228

2 tbsps Mother's apple cider vinegar

3 tbsps fresh organic unsweetened pineapple juice

1/2 tsp fine grain sea salt, to taste

1/2 tsp ground black pepper, to taste

1/2 tsp freshly squeezed lemon juice

1/4 tsp dill weed

Nutrition Facts

Serving Size 1 cup (239g)
Servings Per Container 6

Amount Per Serving

Calories 360   Calories from Fat 210

	% Daily Value*
Total Fat 24g	37%
Saturated Fat 3g	15%
Trans Fat 0g	
Cholesterol 180mg	60%
Sodium 800mg	33%
Total Carbohydrate 30g	10%
Dietary Fiber 5g	20%
Sugars 11g	
Protein 9g	

Vitamin A 250%	•	Vitamin C 20%
Calcium 6%	•	Iron 8%

*Percent Daily Values are based on a 2,000 calorie diet. Your daily values may be higher or lower depending on your calorie needs.

	Calories	2,000	2,500
Total Fat	Less than	65g	80g
Saturated Fat	Less than	20g	25g
Cholesterol	Less than	300mg	300mg
Sodium	Less than	2,400mg	2,400mg
Total Carbohydrate		300g	375g
Dietary Fiber		25g	30g

Calories per gram
Fat 9 • Carbohydrate 4 • Protein 4

Prepare Dijon Mustard and Toasted Pecans, optional.

Prepare Dressing. Mix all ingredients to combine.

Bring a large pot of salted water to a boil. Add sweet potato and cook until tender but still firm, about 30 minutes. Drain, cool, peel and chop; skin will peel off easy with fingers.

In a saucepan, add cold water and egg; cover and bring to a boil over high heat. Remove the saucepan from the heat, and let the egg stand in hot water for 10-12 minutes, to finish cooking. This method is called the Soft Boil. Remove the egg from the water, let cool, peel and chop; set aside in refrigerator.

Combine the sweet potato, egg, celery, shallot, pineapple, and apple. Dressing: combine oil, mustard, vinegar, pineapple juice, sea salt and black pepper; whisk well. Add dressing to the potato mixture, fold carefully to mix. Sprinkle with pecan pieces. Refrigerate and serve chilled.

Servings: 6

Target source of Dietary Fiber, Dietary Fats, Vitamin A, Vitamin C, Manganese, Potassium

Supportive of Immune Health

ORIENTAL VEGETABLES

1 tsp finely chopped fresh ginger root

3 minced garlic clove

2 tbsps coconut oil

1 cup diced organic red bell pepper

1 cup diced organic yellow bell pepper

2 diagonally sliced organic carrots, peeled

2 cups broccoli florets, with stem

10 oz thinly sliced mushrooms

2 tbsps coconut aminos

8 sliced green onions

Nutrition Facts

Serving Size 1 1/4 cup (276g)
Servings Per Container 4

Amount Per Serving

Calories 150	Calories from Fat 70

% Daily Value*

Total Fat 8g	12%
Saturated Fat 6g	30%
Trans Fat 0g	
Cholesterol 0mg	0%
Sodium 220mg	9%
Total Carbohydrate 18g	6%
Dietary Fiber 5g	20%
Sugars 5g	
Protein 5g	

Vitamin A 170%	Vitamin C 290%
Calcium 8%	Iron 8%

*Percent Daily Values are based on a 2,000 calorie diet. Your daily values may be higher or lower depending on your calorie needs.

		Calories	2,000	2,500
Total Fat	Less than		65g	80g
Saturated Fat	Less than		20g	25g
Cholesterol	Less than		300mg	300mg
Sodium	Less than		2,400mg	2,400mg
Total Carbohydrate			300g	375g
Dietary Fiber			25g	30g

Calories per gram:
Fat 9 • Carbohydrate 4 • Protein 4

Heat the oil in a large wok skillet over high heat. When oil is hot, add ginger and garlic and stir-fry for 1 minute. Add pepper and carrot; sauté for 4 minutes until they begin to soften. Add broccoli, mushroom and coconut aminos; stir-fry for 3 minutes until crisp tender.

Remove from the heat and top with green onion.

Servings: 4

Target source of Dietary Fiber, Dietary Fats, Vitamin A, Vitamins B1, B2, B3, B6, Vitamin C, Folate, Vitamin K, Calcium, Copper, Potassium, Phosphorus, Selenium, Zinc

Supportive of Immune and Detoxification Health

ROASTED ASPARAGUS

1 lb asparagus spear

2 tbsps extra virgin olive oil

2 minced garlic clove

1/2 tsp fine grain sea salt

1/2 tsp ground black pepper

2 tbsps freshly squeezed lemon juice or orange juice

Nutrition Facts

Serving Size 1/2 cup (131g)
Servings Per Container 4

Amount Per Serving

Calories 90	Calories from Fat 60

	% Daily Value*
Total Fat 7g	11%
Saturated Fat 1g	5%
Trans Fat 0g	
Cholesterol 0mg	0%
Sodium 290mg	12%
Total Carbohydrate 6g	2%
Dietary Fiber 2g	8%
Sugars 2g	
Protein 3g	

Vitamin A 15%	•	Vitamin C 15%
Calcium 4%	•	Iron 15%

*Percent Daily Values are based on a 2,000 calorie diet. Your daily values may be higher or lower depending on your calorie needs.

	Calories	2,000	2,500
Total Fat	Less than	65g	80g
Saturated Fat	Less than	20g	25g
Cholesterol	Less than	300mg	300mg
Sodium	Less than	2,400mg	2,400mg
Total Carbohydrate		300g	375g
Dietary Fiber		25g	30g

Calories per gram:
Fat 9 • Carbohydrate 4 • Protein 4

Preheat oven to 400° F.

Wash asparagus and cut off tough ends and discard. Lightly coat a sheet pan with cooking spray and lay the asparagus spears out in a single layer. Sprinkle with garlic, sea salt, and black pepper. Sprinkle oil evenly over the spears; roll back and forth until they are all covered with a thin layer of olive oil.

Place the sheet pan in the oven and roast for about 8-10 minutes, depending on how thickness of your asparagus until lightly browned and tender when pierced with a fork. Squeeze fresh lemon juice before serving.

Servings: 4

Target source of Dietary Fiber, Dietary Fats, Vitamin A, Vitamin C, Vitamin K, Folate, B Vitamins, Copper, Iron, Manganese

Supportive of Immune and Detoxification Health

PEAR CIDER BRAISED KALE

5 slices sliced uncured, pastured sliced bacon

1 1/4 cups thinly sliced onion

6 cups chopped organic kale, with stem

1 tbsp Mother's apple cider vinegar

1/3 cup organic pear cider

2 cups diced organic pear, peeled and cored, about 4 pears

1/2 tsp fine grain sea salt

1/4 tsp ground black pepper

Nutrition Facts

Serving Size 1/2 cup (176g)
Servings Per Container 4

Amount Per Serving

Calories 140	Calories from Fat 50

	% Daily Value*
Total Fat 6g	9%
Saturated Fat 2g	10%
Trans Fat 0g	
Cholesterol 10mg	3%
Sodium 500mg	21%
Total Carbohydrate 20g	7%
Dietary Fiber 4g	16%
Sugars 11g	
Protein 5g	

Vitamin A 50%	•	Vitamin C 60%
Calcium 6%	•	Iron 4%

*Percent Daily Values are based on a 2,000 calorie diet. Your daily values may be higher or lower depending on your calorie needs.

		Calories:	2,000	2,500
Total Fat	Less than		65g	80g
Saturated Fat	Less than		20g	25g
Cholesterol	Less than		300mg	300mg
Sodium	Less than		2,400mg	2,400mg
Total Carbohydrate			300g	375g
Dietary Fiber			25g	30g

Calories per gram
Fat 9 • Carbohydrate 4 • Protein 4

Heat a skillet over medium heat; add bacon and cook 5 minutes until crisp. Remove bacon from pan; reserve bacon fat. Crumble bacon, and set aside.

Increase heat to medium-high. Add onion; sauté 5 minutes until translucent. Add kale; sauté 5 minutes until wilted, stirring frequently.

Add vinegar and pear cider; cover sauté 10 minutes, stirring occasionally.

Add pear, sea salt and black pepper; sauté 5 minutes until pear is tender, stirring occasionally.

Crumble bacon and sprinkle over plate.

Tip
Compliments chicken and pork dishes.

Servings: 4

Target source of Dietary Fiber, Vitamin A, Vitamin C, Vitamin K, Folate, Copper, Manganese

Supportive of Immune, Detoxification and Gut Health

ROASTED GARLIC MASHED POTATO AND PARSNIPS

2 roasted garlic clove, unpeeled; Roasted Garlic, page 238

1 tbsps extra virgin olive oil

1 lb diced organic Yukon gold potato, peeled

3/4 cup diced parsnip, peeled

1/4 cup coconut milk, full fat (in a can)

1/8 cup Clarified Butter, page 203

1 tsp fine grain sea salt, to taste

1 tsp ground black pepper, to taste

Nutrition Facts

Serving Size 7oz (192g)
Servings Per Container 4

Amount Per Serving

Calories 310   Calories from Fat 160

	% Daily Value*
Total Fat 18g	28%
Saturated Fat 8g	40%
Trans Fat 0g	
Cholesterol 20mg	7%
Sodium 380mg	16%
Total Carbohydrate 34g	11%
Dietary Fiber 5g	20%
Sugars 4g	
Protein 4g	

Vitamin A 6%	•	Vitamin C 15%
Calcium 6%	•	Iron 10%

*Percent Daily Values are based on a 2,000 calorie diet. Your daily values may be higher or lower depending on your calorie needs.

		Calories	2,000	2,500
Total Fat	Less than		65g	80g
Saturated Fat	Less than		20g	25g
Cholesterol	Less than		300mg	300mg
Sodium	Less than		2,400mg	2,400mg
Total Carbohydrate			300g	375g
Dietary Fiber			25g	30g

Calories per gram
Fat 9 • Carbohydrate 4 • Protein 4

Preheat oven to 350° F.

Prepare Roasted Garlic and Clarified Butter.

Cut the tip of garlic bulb, and discard. Place garlic head into small baking dish and drizzle with extra virgin olive oil. Cover with foil and bake for 20 minutes until tender. Remove from oven and allow cooling. Squeeze the garlic pulp out of peels. Mash with a fork and set aside.

Heat the vegetable broth and sea salt in a saucepan over high heat. Bring to a boil. Add Yukon potatoes and boil about 25-30 minutes until tender. Drain.

Mash the Yukon potatoes and parsnips with a potato masher and return to the saucepan.

Heat coconut milk and clarified butter in a small saucepan at a simmer, not quite boiling; heat through. Add sea salt and pepper, to taste.

Servings: 4

Target source of Dietary Fats, Vitamin C, Chromium, Manganese, Dietary Fiber

308.

ROASTED VEGETABLE MEDLEY

2 cups butternut squash, peeled and cut into 1-inch cubes

2 cups sweet potatoes, peeled and cut into 1-inch cubes

1 cup quartered red onion

3 tbsps extra virgin olive oil

2 tbsps Mother's apple cider vinegar

2 tbsps fresh rosemary or 2 tsps dried rosemary

1 tbsp fresh thyme or 1 tsp dried thyme

1 tsp fine grain sea salt

1/2 tsp ground black pepper

Nutrition Facts

Serving Size 5 oz (136g)
Servings Per Container 7

Amount Per Serving

Calories 130	Calories from Fat 50

	% Daily Value*
Total Fat 6g	**9%**
Saturated Fat 1g	**5%**
Trans Fat 0g	
Cholesterol 0mg	**0%**
Sodium 350mg	**15%**
Total Carbohydrate 20g	**7%**
Dietary Fiber 4g	**16%**
Sugars 5g	
Protein 2g	

Vitamin A 350%	•	Vitamin C 35%
Calcium 6%	•	Iron 4%

*Percent Daily Values are based on a 2,000 calorie diet. Your daily values may be higher or lower depending on your calorie needs.

	Calories	2,000	2,500
Total Fat	Less than	65g	80g
Saturated Fat	Less than	20g	25g
Cholesterol	Less than	300mg	300mg
Sodium	Less than	2,400mg	2,400mg
Total Carbohydrate		300g	375g
Dietary Fiber		25g	30g

Calories per gram:
Fat 9 • Carbohydrate 4 • Protein 4

Preheat oven to 425° F.

In a large bowl, combine the butternut squash, sweet potato and red onion.

In a small bowl, whisk the oil, vinegar, rosemary, thyme, sea salt and black pepper. Pour over vegetables and toss to coat.

Transfer to sheet pan brushed with oil. Bake uncovered for 30-40 minutes until crisp tender and browning; stirring occasionally. If vegetables start to stick, add 1 tablespoon of oil and stir.

Servings: 7

Target source of Dietary Fiber, Vitamin A, Vitamin C, Vitamins B6, Manganese, Potassium

Supportive of Immune Health

SPAGHETTI SQUASH

1 spaghetti squash, medium to large in size, about 5 cups

2 1/2 tbsps Clarified Butter, page 203

1/8 tsp fine grain sea salt

1/8 tsp ground black pepper

Preheat oven to 350° F.

Cut spaghetti squash in half, lengthwise. Place down in a baking sheet pan and fill 1-inch of sheet pan with water. Bake for 30-40 minutes until crisp tender. Do not overcook; squash noodles will become mushy. Allow to cool slightly.

Remove spaghetti squash from baking dish; reserving 3 tbsp of cooking water. Remove seed and discard. Using a fork, scrap the squash to make noodles. Scrap into a mixing bowl and add clarified butter, sea salt and black pepper; toss gently. Add herbs and/or vegetables at this time.

Tips
Add chopped herbs and spices for flavor: chopped herbs (chervil, basil, chive, parsley, thyme, oregano, ginger, sage, cumin) *OR* Add your choice of diced vegetables.

Treat spaghetti squash like pasta.

Stabilize round fruit on a kitchen towel or non-slip surface. Keep your hands away from the knife in case of slip. The outer shell is very tough.

Save seeds to plant in your garden or to toast and eat.

Servings: 4

Target source of Dietary Fiber, Dietary Fats, Vitamin A, Vitamins B3, B6, Vitamin C, Manganese

Supportive of Immune Health

SPAGHETTI SQUASH WITH WALNUT-HERB PESTO

2 large spaghetti squash

2 cups roughly chopped fresh organic arugula

1 cup packed fresh parsley

1/2 cup loosely packed fresh basil

1 tsp fine grain sea salt

1 tsp ground black pepper

1/4 cup chopped walnut, or other nut

3 tbsps extra virgin olive oil

Nutrition Facts

Serving Size 8oz (224g)
Servings Per Container 8

Amount Per Serving

Calories 130	Calories from Fat 70

	% Daily Value*
Total Fat 8g	12%
Saturated Fat 1g	5%
Trans Fat 0g	
Cholesterol 0mg	0%
Sodium 330mg	14%
Total Carbohydrate 14g	5%
Dietary Fiber 3g	12%
Sugars 5g	
Protein 2g	

Vitamin A 25%	•	Vitamin C 30%
Calcium 8%	•	Iron 8%

*Percent Daily Values are based on a 2,000 calorie diet. Your daily values may be higher or lower depending on your calorie needs.

	Calories	2,000	2,500
Total Fat	Less than	65g	80g
Saturated Fat	Less than	20g	25g
Cholesterol	Less than	300mg	300mg
Sodium	Less than	2,400mg	2,400mg
Total Carbohydrate		300g	375g
Dietary Fiber		25g	30g

Calories per gram
Fat 9 • Carbohydrate 4 • Protein 4

Preheat oven to 350° F.

Cut spaghetti squash in half lengthwise. Place face down in a baking dish and fill with 1-inch of water. Bake for 30 minutes until crisp tender. Do not overcook; "noodles" will become mushy.

Meanwhile, prepare pesto by placing arugula, parsley, basil, sea salt and black pepper in a food processor; cover and pulse until chopped. Add walnut; cover and pulse until blended. Gradually add oil in a steady stream. Pulse and hold, 3 seconds at a time until desired consistency is reached; choppy. Place in the refrigerator until ready to use.

Remove spaghetti squash from baking dish; reserving 3 tbsp of cooking water. Using a fork, scrap the inside surface of spaghetti squash and it resembles noodles. Scrap all noodles and add to a mixing bowl.

Mix pesto with reserved water and toss with spaghetti squash to coat. Add spaghetti pesto to a skillet over medium heat and warm throughout. Season with sea salt and pepper, and serve.

Servings: 8

Target source of Vitamin A, Vitamin K, Vitamin C, Manganese, Potassium, Magnesium, Vitamins B6, B3, Folate, Dietary Fiber

Supportive of Immune Health

SPINACH AND ARTICHOKE BAKE

1 1/2 tbsps Clarified Butter, page 203

3/4 tbsp extra virgin olive oil

1 cup organic celery stalk

3/4 cup chopped organic green bell pepper

3/4 cup finely chopped onion

3 minced garlic clove

1 1/2 tbsps coconut flour

3/4 cup coconut milk, full fat, no juice (in a can)

6 cups roughly chopped organic spinach, leaf and stem

1 jar organic artichoke hearts

1/2 tsp fine grain sea salt

1/2 tsp ground cayenne

1/2 tsp organic red pepper flake

Nutrition Facts		
Serving Size 6 oz (166g)		
Servings Per Container 6		
Amount Per Serving		
Calories 150	Calories from Fat 110	
		% Daily Value*
Total Fat 12g		18%
Saturated Fat 8g		40%
Trans Fat 0g		
Cholesterol 10mg		3%
Sodium 370mg		15%
Total Carbohydrate 10g		3%
Dietary Fiber 3g		12%
Sugars 2g		
Protein 3g		
Vitamin A 70%	• Vitamin C 45%	
Calcium 6%	• Iron 15%	

*Percent Daily Values are based on a 2,000 calorie diet. Your daily values may be higher or lower depending on your calorie needs.

	Calories	2,000	2,500
Total Fat	Less than	65g	80g
Saturated Fat	Less than	20g	25g
Cholesterol	Less than	300mg	300mg
Sodium	Less than	2,400mg	2,400mg
Total Carbohydrate		300g	375g
Dietary Fiber		25g	30g

Calories per gram
Fat 9 • Carbohydrate 4 • Protein 4

Preheat oven to 350° F.

Prepare Clarified Butter.

Heat the clarified butter and oil over medium-high heat: sauté celery, red pepper and onion. Add garlic; sauté for 1 minute. Sprinkle and stir in coconut flour until blended; gradually add full fat coconut milk. Bring to a boil; reduce heat to medium-high heat for 2 minutes until thickened. Stir constantly to prevent burning. Reduce heat to medium.

Add spinach, artichoke heart, sea salt, cayenne and red pepper flake. Transfer to a 13 X 9 inch baking dish coated with cooking oil. Bake uncovered for 30-35 minutes. Remove from the oven and let cool slightly.

Servings: 6

Target source of Dietary Fiber, Dietary Fats, Vitamin A, Vitamin B6, Vitamin C, Folate, Vitamin K, Iron, Manganese, Magnesium, Potassium

Supportive of Immune and Detoxification Health

STEAMED CALIFORNIA BLEND

2 cups broccoli florets, with stem

2 cups cauliflower florets, with stem

2 cups sliced carrots, peeled

1 freshly squeezed lemon juice

1/4 tsp fine grain sea salt

1/4 tsp ground black pepper

1 1/2 tbsps mix of fresh herbs (ex. oregano, basil and thyme)

Nutrition Facts

Serving Size 5 1/2 oz (159g)
Servings Per Container 4

Amount Per Serving

Calories 50	Calories from Fat 5

	% Daily Value*
Total Fat 0g	0%
Saturated Fat 0g	0%
Trans Fat 0g	
Cholesterol 0mg	0%
Sodium 210mg	9%
Total Carbohydrate 11g	4%
Dietary Fiber 4g	16%
Sugars 4g	
Protein 3g	

Vitamin A 230%	•	Vitamin C 110%
Calcium 6%	•	Iron 4%

*Percent Daily Values are based on a 2,000 calorie diet. Your daily values may be higher or lower depending on your calorie needs.

	Calories	2,000	2,500
Total Fat	Less than	65g	80g
Saturated Fat	Less than	20g	25g
Cholesterol	Less than	300mg	300mg
Sodium	Less than	2,400mg	2,400mg
Total Carbohydrate		300g	375g
Dietary Fiber		25g	30g

Calories per gram
Fat 9 • Carbohydrate 4 • Protein 4

Heat the water in a saucepan over high heat. Add vegetables to a steamer basket and place the basket on the rim of the saucepan; steam until crisp tender, about 7-10 minutes. Sprinkle with sea salt and black pepper, to taste. Squeeze lemon juice and toss; gently toss with fresh herbs, if you want more flavor.

Servings: 4

Target source of Sulfur, Vitamins B1, B2, B3, B6, Folate, Dietary Fiber, Vitamin C, Vitamin A, Vitamin K, Potassium, Magnesium, Molybdenum, Manganese, Phosphorus

Supportive of Immune and Detoxification Health

VEGETABLE BOLOGNESE

1 cup finely chopped sweet onion

1 chopped zucchini

1 chopped yellow squash

1 med chopped organic green bell pepper

1 med chopped organic red bell pepper

3 sliced organic carrots

1 cup sliced mushroom

1/4 tsp fine grain sea salt

1/4 tsp ground black pepper

Nutrition Facts

Serving Size 3/4 cup (185g)
Servings Per Container 6

Amount Per Serving

Calories 90	Calories from Fat 45

% Daily Value*

Total Fat 5g	8%
Saturated Fat 0.5g	3%
Trans Fat 0g	
Cholesterol 0mg	0%
Sodium 30mg	1%
Total Carbohydrate 11g	4%
Dietary Fiber 3g	12%
Sugars 6g	
Protein 2g	

Vitamin A 140%	•	Vitamin C 100%
Calcium 4%	•	Iron 4%

*Percent Daily Values are based on a 2,000 calorie diet. Your daily values may be higher or lower depending on your calorie needs:

	Calories	2,000	2,500
Total Fat	Less than	65g	80g
Saturated Fat	Less than	20g	25g
Cholesterol	Less than	300mg	300mg
Sodium	Less than	2,400mg	2,400mg
Total Carbohydrate		300g	375g
Dietary Fiber		25g	30g

Calories per gram:
Fat 9 • Carbohydrate 4 • Protein 4

Heat the oil in a skillet over medium-high heat. Add zucchini, squash, bell pepper, carrot and mushroom until crisp tender; add minced garlic last 1 minute of cook time. Season with sea salt and black pepper and serve.

Servings: 6

Target source of Dietary Fiber, Vitamin A, Vitamin C, Vitamin K, B Vitamins, Folate, Copper, Manganese, Molybdenum, Zinc, Potassium, Selenium

Supportive of Immune, Detoxification and Gut Health

SWEET POTATO FRITTERS WITH PISTACHIO-PUMPKIN CRUST

1/4 cup pumpkin seed, hulled

1/2 cup pistachios, unsalted pieces

2 cups diced sweet potato, peeled

4 tbsps coconut oil, for light frying

1/8 tsp fine grain sea salt, to taste

1/8 tsp ground black pepper, to taste

Nutrition Facts

Serving Size 3 small fritters (227g)
Servings Per Container 4

Amount Per Serving

Calories 410   Calories from Fat 210

	% Daily Value*
Total Fat 24g	37%
Saturated Fat 14g	70%
Trans Fat 0g	
Cholesterol 0mg	0%
Sodium 70mg	3%
Total Carbohydrate 45g	15%
Dietary Fiber 8g	32%
Sugars 17g	
Protein 9g	

Vitamin A 2%	•	Vitamin C 2%	
Calcium 2%	•	Iron 8%	

*Percent Daily Values are based on a 2,000 calorie diet. Your daily values may be higher or lower depending on your calorie needs.

	Calories	2,000	2,500
Total Fat	Less than	65g	80g
Saturated Fat	Less than	20g	25g
Cholesterol	Less than	300mg	300mg
Sodium	Less than	2,400mg	2,400mg
Total Carbohydrate		300g	375g
Dietary Fiber		25g	30g

Calories per gram:
Fat 9 • Carbohydrate 4 • Protein 4

Combine pumpkin seeds and pistachios into a food processer; grind to a meal (fine, but still coarse). Set on a separate plate for dredging.

Heat a saucepan over high heat. Add sweet potato and enough water to cover; boil until tender, but not mushy. Drain the water from the saucepan and add a pinch of sea salt and black pepper.

Heat 1 tablespoon of oil in a skillet over medium heat; sauté the sweet potato for 1-2 minutes or until the potato is tender and caramelized. Mash sweet potatoes to desired consistency. Scoop 2-3 tablespoons of potato and press together to form small circular fritters.

Carefully dredge the fritters in pumpkin-pistachio mixture and place on a plate. Repeat with remaining fritters.

Wipe the skillet clean of any potato residue. Heat 2 tablespoon of oil over medium-high heat. When the oil is hot, add fritters; pan-fry for a quick 30-60 seconds on each side. Remove with a slotted spatula.

The potatoes are already cooked so all you need to do is brown or toast the seeded coating. Add Tzatziki Sauce, page 271.

Servings: 4

Target source of Protein, Dietary Fiber, Dietary Fats, Vitamins B1, B6, Copper, Manganese

Supportive of Immune Health and Gut Flora Balance

WILTED MIX CHARD

4 cups regular organic chard

3 cups organic red swiss chard

2 tbsps extra virgin olive oil

2 sliced garlic clove

1/4 cup orange juice

1/4 tsp fine grain sea salt

1/4 tsp ground black pepper

2 tbsps orange zest, garnish

Nutrition Facts

Serving Size 1/2 cup (125g)
Servings Per Container 4

Amount Per Serving

Calories 90	Calories from Fat 60

% Daily Value*

Total Fat 7g	11%
Saturated Fat 1g	5%
Trans Fat 0g	
Cholesterol 0mg	0%
Sodium 250mg	10%
Total Carbohydrate 5g	2%
Dietary Fiber 2g	8%
Sugars 3g	
Protein 2g	

Vitamin A 100%	•	Vitamin C 90%
Calcium 10%	•	Iron 6%

*Percent Daily Values are based on a 2,000 calorie diet. Your daily values may be higher or lower depending on your calorie needs.

	Calories	2,000	2,500
Total Fat	Less than	65g	80g
Saturated Fat	Less than	20g	25g
Cholesterol	Less than	300mg	300mg
Sodium	Less than	2,400mg	2,400mg
Total Carbohydrate		300g	375g
Dietary Fiber		25g	30g

Calories per gram
Fat 9 • Carbohydrate 4 • Protein 4

Rinse chard thoroughly; cut leaves into strips, discard stem.

Heat 2 tablespoons of oil in a large skillet over medium heat. Add garlic; sauté 1 minute. Add chard; cover and sauté 5 minutes; stirring frequently. Add 2 tablespoons of water, if chard looks dry. When chard is wilted, pour in orange juice, sea salt and black pepper; stir to combine. Turn off heat and let set for 2-3 minutes to heat throughout, stirring occasionally. Garnish with orange zest.

Servings: 4

Target source of Dietary Fiber, Vitamin A, Vitamin C, Vitamin K, Vitamin B6, Folate, Calcium, Iron, Magnesium, Potassium, Manganese

Supportive of Immune, Detoxification and Gut Health

ZUCCHINI NOODLES, *how to make*

3 large zucchinis, peeled into ribbons or cut into thin strips
3/4-1 tsp fine grain sea salt, to taste

Wash and cut the ends off the zucchini. With a julienne peeler, lightly run from top to bottom to make even noodles. Continue on all sides rotating to have a secure hold, until you reach the core, where the seeds begin to show. Add to a strainer, sprinkle sea salt throughout and let them sweat for 10 minutes. Heat the oil in a skillet over medium-low heat; sauté for 1-3 minutes.

Tips
Use in place of pasta or to compliment main dish.

Store in the refrigerator in an airtight container for 2-3 days.

Hand cut by cutting into lengthwise slices.

Servings: 6

Target source of Dietary Fiber, Vitamin C, B6, Manganese, Molybdenum

SOUP & SALAD

APPLE AND WALNUT TUNA SALAD

7 ozs Tuna Steak, page 133

1/2 cup chopped organic apple

1 tsp freshly squeezed lemon juice

1/4 cup roughly chopped walnuts

1/2 cup Clean Mayonnaise, page 225

1/8 tsp fine grain sea salt

1/8 tsp ground black pepper

Nutrition Facts		
Serving Size 5 oz (152g)		
Servings Per Container 4		
Amount Per Serving		
Calories 360	Calories from Fat 260	
		% Daily Value*
Total Fat 30g		46%
Saturated Fat 12g		60%
Trans Fat 0g		
Cholesterol 75mg		25%
Sodium 150mg		6%
Total Carbohydrate 4g		1%
Dietary Fiber 1g		4%
Sugars 2g		
Protein 25g		
Vitamin A 2%	•	Vitamin C 4%
Calcium 2%	•	Iron 2%

*Percent Daily Values are based on a 2,000 calorie diet. Your daily values may be higher or lower depending on your calorie needs.

	Calories	2,000	2,500
Total Fat	Less than	65g	80g
Saturated Fat	Less than	20g	25g
Cholesterol	Less than	300mg	300mg
Sodium	Less than	2,400mg	2,400mg
Total Carbohydrate		300g	375g
Dietary Fiber		25g	30g

Calories per gram
Fat 9 • Carbohydrate 4 • Protein 4

Prepare Tuna Steak and Clean Mayonnaise.

Combine all ingredients in a bowl and mix well.

SERVING OPTIONS
Tortillas, page 189; pick a flavor.

Serve over choice of leafy greens

Use as a dip for Chips, pick your flavor

Servings: 4

Target source of Protein, Dietary Fats, Copper, Manganese

Supportive of Immune Health

BABY GREEN SALAD WITH ORANGES AND OLIVES

1 1/2 tbsps extra virgin olive oil

1 tbsp orange juice

1 tbsp balsamic vinegar

6 cups chopped organic mesclun salad greens

4 slices organic red onion, separated into rings

1 cup sectioned orange

1/3 cup sliced organic kalamata olives, 4 oz can

1/4 tsp fine sea salt

1/4 tsp ground black pepper

Nutrition Facts

Serving Size 5 1/2 oz (154g)
Servings Per Container 4

Amount Per Serving	
Calories 100	Calories from Fat 50

	% Daily Value*
Total Fat 6g	9%
Saturated Fat 0.5g	3%
Trans Fat 0g	
Cholesterol 0mg	0%
Sodium 380mg	16%
Total Carbohydrate 9g	3%
Dietary Fiber 1g	4%
Sugars 5g	
Protein 1g	

Vitamin A 120%	•	Vitamin C 50%
Calcium 2%	•	Iron 4%

*Percent Daily Values are based on a 2,000 calorie diet. Your daily values may be higher or lower depending on your calorie needs.

	Calories	2,000	2,500
Total Fat	Less than	65g	80g
Saturated Fat	Less than	20g	25g
Cholesterol	Less than	300mg	300mg
Sodium	Less than	2,400mg	2,400mg
Total Carbohydrate		300g	375g
Dietary Fiber		25g	30g

Calories per gram
Fat 9 • Carbohydrate 4 • Protein 4

Prepare Dressing
In a small mixing bowl, combine oil, orange juice and vinegar and whisk till mixed thoroughly.

Salad
Place greens in a large salad bowl. Pour in dressing and gently fold into mix. Do not over mix.

Add greens to each plate and layer with onion, orange sections, and olives. Lightly sprinkle with sea salt and black pepper.

Servings: 4

Target source of Vitamin A, Vitamin C, Potassium, Dietary Fiber

Supportive of Immune and Gut Health

327.

CARIBBEAN CHICKEN SALAD WITH CASHEWS

SALAD

3 cups shredded free-range thighs, boneless, skinless

1/4 cup cashew

1/3 cup Clean Mayonnaise, page 225

1/4 cup Raspberry Honey Maple Chutney, page 247

1 tbsp coconut sugar

2 tbsps Mother's apple cider vinegar

1 1/2 tsps curry powder

6 cups shredded organic romaine lettuce, or other leafy green

1/4 cup sliced green onion

3/4 cup diced mango, peeled

1/2 cup chopped organic red bell pepper

1 cup fresh raspberry, garnish

1/2 cup cashew, garnish

SALAD DRESSING

2 tsps freshly squeezed lemon juice

1 tsp balsamic vinegar

1/2 tsp Dijon Mustard

3 tbsps extra virgin olive oil

1/4 tsp fine grain sea salt

1/4 tsp ground black pepper to, taste

Nutrition Facts		
Serving Size 1 cup (378g)		
Servings Per Container 4		
Amount Per Serving		
Calories 200	Calories from Fat 50	
		% Daily Value*
Total Fat 6g		9%
Saturated Fat 1.5g		8%
Trans Fat 0g		
Cholesterol 25mg		8%
Sodium 170mg		7%
Total Carbohydrate 31g		10%
Dietary Fiber 6g		24%
Sugars 12g		
Protein 10g		
Vitamin A 280%	•	Vitamin C 180%
Calcium 10%	•	Iron 15%

*Percent Daily Values are based on a 2,000 calorie diet. Your daily values may be higher or lower depending on your calorie needs.

	Calories	2,000	2,500
Total Fat	Less than	65g	80g
Saturated Fat	Less than	20g	25g
Cholesterol	Less than	300mg	300mg
Sodium	Less than	2,400mg	2,400mg
Total Carbohydrate		300g	375g
Dietary Fiber		25g	30g

Calories per gram
Fat 9 • Carbohydrate 4 • Protein 4

Preheat oven to 400° F.

Prepare Clean Mayonnaise and Raspberry Honey Nut Chutney.

Wash chicken and trim fat. Place on a sheet pan sprayed with cooking oil. Bake for 15-20 minutes. Internal thermometer reads 165° F, at the thickest part. Shred with a fork and set aside.

Dressing: in a food processor combine cashew, mayonnaise, chutney, coconut sugar, vinegar and curry powder; mix until smooth.

Toss romaine lettuce with green onions; divide among plates. Add chicken, mango and bell pepper. Mix in chutney and dressing. Garnish with fresh raspberry and cashews.

Servings: 4

Target source of Protein, Vitamin A, Vitamin C, Vitamin K, Folate, Dietary Fiber

Supportive of Immune and Neurological Health

CREAMY GINGER-CARROT SOUP

1 cup diced sweet onion

2 minced garlic clove

2 tbsps fresh grated ginger

1 tbsp extra virgin olive oil, more as needed

1 1/2 cups chopped organic green apple

5 cups chopped organic carrot, peeled

4 cups organic vegetable broth

1/4 tsp fresh grated nutmeg

1/4 tsp fine grain sea salt, to taste

1/4 tsp ground black pepper, to taste

1 tbsp extra virgin olive oil

1/8 cup parsley, garnish

Nutrition Facts

Serving Size 12oz (328g)
Servings Per Container 6

Amount Per Serving

Calories 110	Calories from Fat 25

% Daily Value*

Total Fat 2.5g	4%
Saturated Fat 0g	0%
Trans Fat 0g	
Cholesterol 0mg	0%
Sodium 500mg	21%
Total Carbohydrate 20g	7%
Dietary Fiber 5g	20%
Sugars 11g	
Protein 2g	

Vitamin A 360%	•	Vitamin C 15%
Calcium 4%	•	Iron 2%

*Percent Daily Values are based on a 2,000 calorie diet. Your daily values may be higher or lower depending on your calorie needs.

	Calories	2,000	2,500
Total Fat	Less than	65g	80g
Saturated Fat	Less than	20g	25g
Cholesterol	Less than	300mg	300mg
Sodium	Less than	2,400mg	2,400mg
Total Carbohydrate		300g	375g
Dietary Fiber		25g	30g

Calories per gram
Fat 9 • Carbohydrate 4 • Protein 4

Heat 1 tablespoon of oil over medium heat. Add onion; sauté for about 5 minutes until translucent. Add garlic and ginger; sauté for 2 minutes. Add apple and carrot; sauté for 3 minutes. Add the vegetable broth and fresh nutmeg; bring to a boil over high heat, stirring occasionally. Reduce heat to medium-low and simmer for 20 minutes until tender.

Pour this mixture into a blender, only half full; may need to be done in a couple of batches. Contents will be hot; remove the lid cap. Add nutmeg, sea salt and black pepper; blend until smooth. *Add more broth, if you want a thinner soup; blend well.

Ladle into a bowl, drizzle with a little extra-virgin olive oil, and garnish with parsley.

Servings: 5

Target source of Vitamin A, Vitamin B6, Vitamin C, Vitamin K, Dietary Fiber

Supportive of Immune, Heart and Gut Health

FREE RANGE CHICKEN SALAD

6 free-range boneless chicken thighs, cut in cubes or shredded

1/4 tsp fine grain sea salt

1/2 tsp ground black pepper

1/2 tsp ground paprika

1 diced organic green apple

1 diced organic red apple

1 finely chopped onion

1 finely chopped organic celery stalk

3/4 cup halved organic grape

1/2-3/4 cup Clean Mayonnaise, page 225

6-10 organic romaine lettuce leaf

1/8 bunch finely chopped parsley, garnish

4 tbsps chopped walnut, garnish

Nutrition Facts

Serving Size 7 oz (204g)
Servings Per Container 8

Amount Per Serving

Calories 230	Calories from Fat 140

	% Daily Value*
Total Fat 16g	25%
Saturated Fat 6g	30%
Trans Fat 0g	
Cholesterol 60mg	20%
Sodium 135mg	6%
Total Carbohydrate 14g	5%
Dietary Fiber 3g	12%
Sugars 9g	
Protein 13g	

Vitamin A 100%	•	Vitamin C 8%
Calcium 4%	•	Iron 8%

*Percent Daily Values are based on a 2,000 calorie diet. Your daily values may be higher or lower depending on your calorie needs.

	Calories:	2,000	2,500
Total Fat	Less than	65g	80g
Saturated Fat	Less than	20g	25g
Cholesterol	Less than	300mg	300mg
Sodium	Less than	2,400mg	2,400mg
Total Carbohydrate		300g	375g
Dietary Fiber		25g	30g

Calories per gram:
Fat 9 • Carbohydrate 4 • Protein 4

Preheat oven to 400° F.

Prepare Clean Mayonnaise.

Sprinkle chicken with sea salt, black pepper and paprika on both sides. Bake chicken for 18-20 minutes; let cool and then cut into medium dice or shred. Internal temperature should read 165° F, at the thickest part.

In a small bowl, add apple, onion and celery and grapes in half. Add mayonnaise to your desired coating. Serve over romaine lettuce. Garnish with parsley and walnut.

Tips
For easier shredding, pulse chicken in a food processor.

Freeze for later: package chicken and fruit separately.

Servings: 6

Target source of Protein, Dietary Fats, Dietary Fiber, Folate, Vitamin A, Vitamin K, Manganese, Biotin

Supportive of Immune, Detoxification and Gut Health

MINT CITRUS SALAD

MINT-LEMON VINAIGRETTE

1/4 cup extra virgin olive oil

2 tbsps coconut sugar

1 tsp zested lemon peel

1 tbsp freshly squeezed lemon juice

1/4 tsp fine grain sea salt

CITRUS SALAD

6 cups shredded organic romaine lettuce

3 large sectioned oranges, peeled

1 large sectioned pink grapefruit, peeled

2 tbsps sliced medium green onion

1 tbsp freshly chopped mint leaves

1/8 cup freshly chopped mint leaves, garnish

Nutrition Facts

Serving Size 7oz (197g)
Servings Per Container 6

Amount Per Serving

Calories 160   Calories from Fat 80

% Daily Value*

Total Fat 10g — 15%

Saturated Fat 1.5g — 8%

Trans Fat 0g

Cholesterol 0mg — 0%

Sodium 105mg — 4%

Total Carbohydrate 21g — 7%

Dietary Fiber 3g — 12%

Sugars 17g

Protein 2g

Vitamin A 70% • Vitamin C 120%

Calcium 6% • Iron 2%

*Percent Daily Values are based on a 2,000 calorie diet. Your daily values may be higher or lower depending on your calorie needs.

	Calories	2,000	2,500
Total Fat	Less than	65g	80g
Saturated Fat	Less than	20g	25g
Cholesterol	Less than	300mg	300mg
Sodium	Less than	2,400mg	2,400mg
Total Carbohydrate		300g	375g
Dietary Fiber		25g	30g

Calories per gram:
Fat 9 • Carbohydrate 4 • Protein 4

Prepare Mint-Citrus Salad.

Combine oil, coconut sugar, lemon peel, lemon juice and sea salt in an airtight container with a lid. Cover and shake well.

Section the orange and grapefruit; place in a medium bowl with mint and onion. Gently toss, cover and refrigerate for 2 hours, longer if needed.

Shred lettuce and place in a large mixing bowl and top with citrus mixture. Add mint-lemon vinaigrette and lightly toss to coat.

Serve promptly or add citrus mixture and vinaigrette at service time. Garnish with fresh mint leaves.

Servings: 6

Target source of Vitamin A, Vitamin C, Vitamin K, Dietary Fiber, Unsaturated Fats

Supportive of Phase 1 Liver Detoxification and Gut Health

SPICY BEET AND CARROT SALAD

1 lb diced organic carrot, peeled

1 cup diced yellow onion, peeled

1 lb diced beet, peeled

1 tbsp local raw honey

1 tsp organic chipotle chili powder

1 tsp Dijon Mustard, page 228

1 tbsp extra virgin olive oil

1/2 cup brewed green tea

2 tsps Mother's apple cider vinegar

1/8 tsp fine grain sea salt

6 cups organic arugula lettuce leaf

Nutrition Facts

Serving Size 1 cup (235g)

Servings Per Container 6

Amount Per Serving

Calories 100 Calories from Fat 25

% Daily Value*

Total Fat 3g — 5%

Saturated Fat 0g — 0%

Trans Fat 0g

Cholesterol 0mg — 0%

Sodium 280mg — 12%

Total Carbohydrate 19g — 6%

Dietary Fiber 4g — 16%

Sugars 12g

Protein 2g

Vitamin A 270% • Vitamin C 25%

Calcium 10% • Iron 10%

*Percent Daily Values are based on a 2,000 calorie diet. Your daily values may be higher or lower depending on your calorie needs.

	Calories	2,000	2,500
Total Fat	Less than	65g	80g
Saturated Fat	Less than	20g	25g
Cholesterol	Less than	300mg	300mg
Sodium	Less than	2,400mg	2,400mg
Total Carbohydrate		300g	375g
Dietary Fiber		25g	30g

Calories per gram:

Fat 9 • Carbohydrate 4 • Protein 4

Preheat oven to 450° F.

Prepare Dijon Mustard.

Brew green tea. Boil 1 cup of water and add green tea bag. Let tea bag simmer for 10-15 minutes.

On a sheet pan sprayed with cooking oil, place carrot and onion one side and beet on the other side; to keep the red beet color from bleeding onto the carrot and onion. Cover sheet pan with aluminum foil and bake for 20 minutes. Uncover and bake for an additional 20 minutes.

Prepare dressing: whisk together honey, chipotle chili powder, Dijon mustard, oil, green tea, vinegar and sea salt.

Remove sheet pan from the oven and set aside to cool; about 2 minutes. Transfer vegetables to a large mixing bowl. Add dressing and softly fold to mix. Spoon vegetable mixture over arugula leaf and serve.

Servings: 4

Target source of Dietary Fiber, Vitamin B6, Folate, Vitamin A, Vitamin C, Vitamin K, Manganese, Iron, Potassium

Supportive of Immune, Detoxification and Gut Health

SPICY GINGER KALE SALAD

1 cup Spicy Ginger Sauce, page 266

2 tbsps coconut oil

8 cups chopped kale, chop stems separately

1 tbsp chopped Pickled Ginger, page 236

1 cup chopped red onion

1/2 cup crumbled walnut

Spicy Ginger Sauce Ingredients

2 tbsps creamy almond butter

1/2 cup water

1 tbsp tahini sauce

1 tsp sesame oil

1 tbsp Pickled Ginger, page 236

1 tsp chopped fresh ginger

1 minced garlic cloves

2-3 tsps coconut amino

1 tsp freshly squeezed lemon juice

2 tsps maple syrup, grade B

5 dashes organic cayenne, optional

1/8 tsp fine grain sea salt

1/8 tsp ground black pepper, to taste

Nutrition Facts

Serving Size 7oz (200g)
Servings Per Container 4

Amount Per Serving

Calories 240   Calories from Fat 150

% Daily Value*

Total Fat 17g	26%
Saturated Fat 2.5g	13%
Trans Fat 0g	
Cholesterol 0mg	0%
Sodium 200mg	8%
Total Carbohydrate 16g	5%
Dietary Fiber 6g	24%
Sugars 6g	
Protein 8g	

Vitamin A 70%	•	Vitamin C 40%
Calcium 35%	•	Iron 10%

*Percent Daily Values are based on a 2,000 calorie diet. Your daily values may be higher or lower depending on your calorie needs.

	Calories	2,000	2,800
Total Fat	Less than	65g	80g
Saturated Fat	Less than	20g	25g
Cholesterol	Less than	300mg	300mg
Sodium	Less than	2,400mg	2,400mg
Total Carbohydrate		300g	375g
Dietary Fiber		25g	30g

Calories per gram
Fat 9 • Carbohydrate 4 • Protein 4

Prepare Spicy Ginger Sauce and Pickled Ginger.

Wash kale and place in strainer to dry out; remove excess water with a clean towel paper towel.

Heat 2 tablespoons of oil over medium-high heat. Add spicy ginger sauce ingredients; stirring constantly until incorporated. Reduce heat to medium; simmer for about 2 minutes, stirring frequently.

Reduce heat to low. Add kale stem pieces and 4 cups of the kale leaves; gently mix into skillet mixture. The kale will begin to wilt.

Turn off the heat and add the remaining amount of kale. Add the pickled ginger, red onion and walnut; gently toss the kale salad for 1-3 minutes until all kale has wilted and ingredients are mixed well. Serve warm or cover and chill in the refrigerator until service.

Tips
For thicker sauce coverage, fold in the Kale a little at a time or double the recipe.

Store the salad in an airtight container for up to 4 days, for a more flavorful taste.

Servings: 4

Excellent source of Vitamin C, Vitamin A, Manganese

Target source of Calcium, Folate, Dietary Fiber, Dietary Fats, Potassium, Copper

Supportive of Immune and Detoxification Health, and Gut Flora Balance

SPICY GINGER KALE SALAD WITH PORTOBELLO AND PINE NUTS

4 cups Cauliflower Rice, page 286

2 tbsps extra virgin olive oil

4 cups Spicy Ginger Kale Salad, page 338

1 1/2 cups thinly sliced Portobello mushrooms

1/2 cup sliced sweet onion

1 tsp coconut aminos

1/4 tsp fine grain sea salt

1/4 tsp ground black pepper

2 tsps sesame oil, garnish

2 tbsps pine nuts, Toasted Nuts, page 241

1/4 cup lightly chopped fresh cilantro

Nutrition Facts

Serving Size 10oz (278g)
Servings Per Container 8

Amount Per Serving

Calories 230   Calories from Fat 140

% Daily Value*

Total Fat 16g	25%
Saturated Fat 4.5g	23%
Trans Fat 0g	
Cholesterol 10mg	3%
Sodium 150mg	6%
Total Carbohydrate 17g	6%
Dietary Fiber 7g	28%
Sugars 7g	
Protein 8g	

Vitamin A 40%	•	Vitamin C 110%
Calcium 20%	•	Iron 10%

*Percent Daily Values are based on a 2,000 calorie diet. Your daily values may be higher or lower depending on your calorie needs.

		Calories	2,000	2,900
Total Fat	Less than		65g	80g
Saturated Fat	Less than		20g	25g
Cholesterol	Less than		300mg	300mg
Sodium	Less than		2,400mg	2,400mg
Total Carbohydrate			300g	375g
Dietary Fiber			25g	30g

Calories per gram:
Fat 9 • Carbohydrate 4 • Protein 4

Prepare the Cauliflower Rice, Spicy Ginger Kale Salad and Toasted Nuts.

Heat 2 tablespoons of oil over medium-high heat. Add cauliflower rice, sprinkle with sea salt and black pepper; toss to coat and heat through, about 3-5 minutes.

Heat the oil in a skillet over medium heat. When oil is hot, add the mushroom and sweet onion: sauté for about 5 minutes until tender.

Add 1 teaspoon of coconut aminos, sea salt and black pepper; sauté 1 minute. Add kale salad and cauliflower rice; gently toss, allowing all flavors to infuse; sauté for 2 minutes. Remove skillet and let mixture set for 3 minutes; tossing occasionally.

Garnish with toasted pine nuts and fresh cilantro. Drizzle with sesame oil; best served warm.

Servings: 4

SPRING VEGETABLE MINESTRONE

6 pressed garlic clove

2 tsps ground paprika

1 tbsp extra virgin olive oil

1 1/2 cups diced white onion

1 tsp fine grain sea salt, divided

1/4 cup organic tomato paste

1 diced organic tomato

8 cups organic vegetable stock

1 1/2 cups sliced yellow squash, peeled

1 1/2 cups rhubarb, peeled and cut into 1/2-inch cubes

1 1/2 cups turnip, peeled and cut into 1/2-inch cubes

2 sliced organic carrot

3/4 tsp coarsely ground black peppercorn or medley

1 cup trimmed organic sugar snap peas, cut diagonally into
    1/2-inch pieces

1/2 cup chopped fresh basil or 2 tbsps dried basil

1/4 tsp fresh grated ginger; added last 20 minutes of cook time

1 1/2 cups Sour Cream, page 239, garnish

1 cup green onion, garnish

Nutrition Facts

Serving Size 2 cups (509g)
Servings Per Container 8

Amount Per Serving

Calories 310   Calories from Fat 210

% Daily Value*

Total Fat 24g	37%
Saturated Fat 13g	65%
Trans Fat 0g	
Cholesterol 25mg	8%
Sodium 980mg	41%
Total Carbohydrate 21g	7%
Dietary Fiber 5g	20%
Sugars 11g	
Protein 4g	

Vitamin A 80%	•	Vitamin C 50%
Calcium 8%	•	Iron 15%

*Percent Daily Values are based on a 2,000 calorie diet. Your daily values may be higher or lower depending on your calorie needs.

	Calories	2,000	2,500
Total Fat	Less than	65g	80g
Saturated Fat	Less than	20g	25g
Cholesterol	Less than	300mg	300mg
Sodium	Less than	2,400mg	2,400mg
Total Carbohydrate		300g	375g
Dietary Fiber		25g	30g

Calories per gram
Fat 9 • Carbohydrate 4 • Protein 4

Prepare Sour Cream, optional.

Heat the oil in a 5-qt stockpot or Dutch oven over medium-low. Add garlic and paprika; heat until fragrant, about 60-90 seconds. Add onion and 1/2 tsp sea salt; sauté 5-7 minutes or until tender.

Add tomato paste; stir until combined. Add vegetable stock and tomato. Bring to a simmer; reduce to low heat and cook 18-20 minutes until flavors are blended, skimming occasionally.

Meanwhile, dice squash and cut peas on a bias into 1/2 inch (1 cm) pieces. Turn heat to high, add squash, rhubarb, turnip, carrot, pea, basil and remaining 1/2 teaspoon of sea salt and black pepper corn to stock pot; bring to a boil. Cover and cook an additional 30-45 minutes, until vegetables are soft and soup is cooked through.

Garnish with sour cream and green onions.

Tip
Sugar snap peas contain fibrous strings on the sides. Before preparing this recipe, twist off bottom stems and pull to remove.

Yield: 12 cups

Target source of Dietary Fats, Vitamin A, Vitamin C, Vitamin K, Manganese

Supportive of Immune Health

"Let food be thy medicine and medicine be thy food."

--Hippocrates

NUTRITION EXTRAS

Shoot For Healthy Nutrition Tips

Good nutrition is fundamental to healing and promoting optimal health. Food can be a persons medicine or poison depending on where it comes from and how it acts in the body. Each individual is different so there is no one size fits all diet plan. This book is dedicated toward wholesome foods void of toxicity and high in nutrient content. Three major concepts behind these recipes are immune, gut health, and detoxification support. Many foods overlap and address all of these concepts.

Learning to cook can be a great way to incorporate more healing foods while reducing your food budget. In the past 50-70 years, more people have turned to convenience foods due to their fast paced lifestyles and low prices. Unfortunately, these foods are highly processed, high in omega 6 oils, trans fats, toxins, and low in nutrients. We hope to provide fairly easy to make recipes high in nutrients that support your goals to reduce inflammation and restore body balance.

Immune Support

These foods support the immune system by helping to reduce inflammation and excessive oxidation. Oxidative stress can damage cells triggering disease, and accelerate the aging process. Excessive inflammation is typically at the root of most illness and disease. Antioxidant rich foods help reduce and quench the free radical damage done by oxidative stress. Oxidative stress can lead to multiple disease states such as heart disease, cancer, joint and bone deterioration, neurological illness, mood and mental health disorders, autoimmune, etc.

Fat soluble antioxidants: Vitamins A, D, E, K (stored in liver and adipose, may not need daily)
Water soluble antioxidant: Vitamin C, B-complex Vitamins (need daily replenishment)

Reference SpectraCell Laboratories Micronutrient Functions, Deficiency and Symptoms, pages 351-353.

There are also foods and spices that help support the immune system by reducing inflammation. Foods that contain omega 3 fatty acids are a natural ant-inflammatory. The general population has an excessive omega 6 problem. The body prefers to have a balanced ratio of fatty acids to work optimally. It is believed that our ancestors, who ate from the earth and close to bodies of water, had a healthier balance of omega 6 to 3 ratios (2:1) compared to today. Convenience and fast foods are loaded with omega 6 oils because they help increase shelf life and they tend to be inexpensive. It's estimated that the population has an omega 6 to 3 ratio closer to 23:1. The excess of omega 6 in the body increases inflammation and stimulates the immune system. We need to focus on reducing omega 6 and increasing omega 3 fatty acids. Fish oils are commonly used today as a natural anti-inflammatory and alternative to other food sources. Examples of omega 3 rich foods include fatty fish like salmon and tuna, grass fed meats and poultry, eggs, algae, basil, oregano, marjoram, flax seed, chia seeds, and walnuts.

Coconut oil is another important fat involved in supporting immune function. It is a medium chain fatty acid that contains lauric acid. Lauric acid is converted to monolaurin. Monolaurin has antiviral properties. It binds to the lipid part of the virus inhibiting it's attachment to the cell, therefore inhibiting infection. Monolaurin has also shown anti-bacterial and antifungal properties.

346.

Fresh Fruits and Vegetables are high in antioxidants, fiber and many other nutrients that help keep the body in balance. Regular intake of 5-9 servings per day help to regulate blood sugars, provide fiber for bowel and heart health, and reduce inflammation. It's best to eat from the rainbow and include a variety of colors in your meal planning. Examples of high antioxidant fruits and vegetables include raspberries and blueberries, red grapes, dark green vegetables, sweet potatoes and other orange vegetables.

Mushrooms contain beta-glucans that are known to boost immune function. Maitaki mushrooms are now used as medicinal support for reduction of cancer tumors. Beta-glucans influence macrophages and other immune regulation. Fresh Garlic is well known for its antibacterial and antiviral properties, especially topically. It contains allicin which helps reduce tumor growth in cancer.

Turmeric is known for its anti-inflammatory properties especially in joint and soft tissue repair. It has almost 5 times more antioxidant power than vitamin C.

Cinnamon not only helps improve insulin sensitivity, but it's also antimicrobial. It can help reduce E.coli infection. Ginger contains gingerols that are known for their anti-inflammatory, antioxidant and anti-cancer effects. It's especially known for its support in reducing joint pain and reducing nausea.

These are just a few of the major foods that support immune function, but I want to mention that stress is probably the primary reason for increases in inflammation. Emotional, physical (including environmental) stress increases oxidative stress at the cellular level. It is important to be mindful of your thoughts, movement and toxic load.

Gut Support

Gut health is fundamental to overall health. About 85% of your immune function lies in your gut. It's involved in digestion and assimilation of nutrients that are essential for cellular function and reduction in disease risk.

Stress, food sensitivities, food allergens, medications, alcohol, caffeine, viral and bacterial infections can all contribute to a poorly functioning gut. They may contribute to excessive inflammation of the intestines and what's known as "leaky gut".

Leaky gut is when an offending protein causes an immune response leading to damage of the intestinal wall. This can cause the gut junctions that normally remain tight keeping large proteins and food particles from entering the blood stream, to widen. The microvilli that are like little fingers that line the gut and help "grab" onto the nutrients it needs can become flattened. This process inhibits the absorption of nutrients and causes an increase in inflammatory processes that can affect the entire body. Important beneficial microbes can get wiped out leaving you susceptible to bacterial overgrowth and infection.

347.

Some side effects of an inflamed gut are headaches, skin rashes, bloating, gas, diarrhea, constipation, joint pain, and a compromised immune system.

It is important to explore food sensitivities when it comes to the health of your gut. Elimination diet trials have been used for decades as a way to determine what foods may be offending the gut. The most common foods today are gluten containing products and milk products but you can have food sensitivity to just about any food. Food sensitivity testing has become even more accurate over the past 10 years and can be a great tool in determining what foods are affecting you personally.

Emotional stress also contributes to a reduction in stomach acid and poor digestion. The stomach is meant to be acidic because that's required for optimal digestion of foods and balance of gut microbes. The over use of antacids can make digestion and gut health even worse!! Identifying foods and substances that are affecting the gut is a better option than covering up a symptom with acid lowering drugs.

A way to restore the gut is to eliminate offending substances, replenish the gut with healthy bacteria, support digestion with digestive enzymes and high fiber foods, reduce stress and toxins, and supply gut healing foods.

Fermented foods, such as kefir, raw fermented sauerkraut, pickles, and olives, contain enzymes and healthy bacteria known as probiotics that aid in digestion as well as support gut lining health. Probiotics play many roles in the body. Immune regulation is just one of their many jobs.

Raw Honey contains propolis which is an antimicrobial. It also contains phenols that help boost immune function. It has a bifido effect meaning it actually supports the growth of beneficial gut bacteria.

Coconut oil as mentioned earlier has antibacterial influence and may contribute to gut bacteria balance. This also supports constipation relief.

Fiber found in fruits, vegetables, legumes, whole grains, nuts and seeds help support cholesterol levels as well as elimination of toxins. Regular bowel movements are extremely important in the reduction of toxic load in the body and gut related cancers and illness. Green apples contain malic acid which helps protect and restore the gut lining.

Butter and Ghee contain butyrate which influences T Lymphocytes boosting immune function and improving colon health. It also helps support K2 levels which are involved in gut and bone health.

Detoxification

Detoxification is the natural process your body goes through to eliminate toxins and byproducts not necessary for health and cellular function. Detoxification is a hot topic today because more and more evidence is coming out about the effects of poor detoxification, issues with detoxification of medications, and the levels of toxins in our environment. We have become more aware of just how toxic our environment is through the work of the ***Environmental Working Group*** and many truth seeking organizations.

348.

The agricultural and industrial revolution brought on a wave of innovation but it also brought about air pollution, heavy metals, arsenic, plastics, pesticides, phthalates, dioxins and flame retardants that are extremely persistent and will most likely never go away.

Umbilical cord studies in infants have shown just how toxic our environment really is. We have seen an increase in illness related to autoimmune, hormone imbalance, and oxidative stress which may very well be linked to the toxic load of our environment. A great number of detoxification protocols and supplements have hit the market with thousands testifying to improvement in health and symptoms after completing these protocols.

So the question is not "am I toxic?" The new question is now "how toxic am I and what can I do about it?" Nutrition, gut and liver health, genetic influence, and toxic load all contribute to how well you detox your environment and own metabolic byproducts. The primary organ involved in detoxification is your liver. It's called the "power house" of organs because it is involved in so many different tasks. The gut, kidneys, gallbladder, respiratory, lymphatic and endocrine system are also involved in detoxification. You will notice in the picture of the liver below just how many vitamins, minerals and amino acids are involved in liver detoxification. If you are utilizing these nutrients and not replenishing them, it may create a sluggish liver and whole body burden. Some people have genetic mutations requiring more or less of these nutrients. There is genetic testing and nutrient deficiency testing available for further investigation.

All toxins enter the liver through the first phase as fat soluble compounds. They are converted into an even more reactive toxin compound before the second phase where it is then converted into a water soluble compound for elimination through the kidneys, bowels, lungs and skin. Each step requires specific nutrients.

Sulfur rich vegetables, or cruciferous vegetables, are super detox foods because they influence both phases of the liver detoxification process. These foods are known as "anti cancer" vegetables. These foods contain compounds such as cysteine and sulfur which are critical for the second phase of the liver. They may also contain indole -3 -carbinol which is used especially for clearing excess estrogen.

Green vegetables are very high in antioxidants, low in sugar, and contain numerous vitamins and minerals that support liver, gallbladder, and kidney detoxification.

Beets are known for their support of the gall bladder by thinning the bile. They also contain pectin and betaine which support the clearance of toxins from the liver.

Nuts and Seeds contain nutrients such as amino acids, calcium, magnesium, and fiber. Healthy fats also help support normal cholesterol levels and keep the liver healthy.

Milk Thistle helps protect the liver during the detoxification process.

Chlorella and Cilantro help bind to heavy metals for elimination. They are also high in antioxidants and aid in cellular repair.

Animal proteins that are hormone free pasture raised animals contain cysteine which helps support glutathione levels. This is a major antioxidant needed to perform detoxification. Caution with over cooked and chard meats. This may actually contribute to more toxins.

Low to moderate fat intake is best when supporting detoxification. Fats have a high affinity for toxins. Animals store toxins in their fatty tissue just as we do. Butters and oils stored in plastic containers are most likely high in BPA toxins. Healthy fats found in nuts, seeds, avocados and other foods are highly beneficial for cellular and neurological health. Almost all wholesome foods with the least amount of processing will contain ingredients and compounds that support the detoxification process. It is how we put these foods together that can make the biggest difference in restoring liver health and reducing oxidative stress throughout the body.

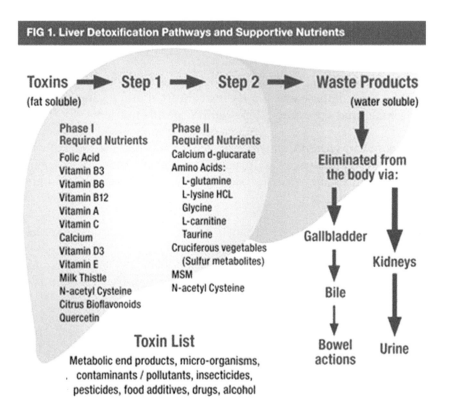

FIG 1. Liver Detoxification Pathways and Supportive Nutrients

Toxins → Step 1 → Step 2 → Waste Products
(fat soluble)   (water soluble)

Phase I
Required Nutrients
Folic Acid
Vitamin B3
Vitamin B6
Vitamin B12
Vitamin A
Vitamin C
Calcium
Vitamin D3
Vitamin E
Milk Thistle
N-acetyl Cysteine
Citrus Bioflavonoids
Quercetin

Phase II
Required Nutrients
Calcium d-glucarate
Amino Acids:
    L-glutamine
    L-lysine HCL
    Glycine
    L-carnitine
    Taurine
Cruciferous vegetables
    (Sulfur metabolites)
MSM
N-acetyl Cysteine

Eliminated from
the body via:

Gallbladder   Kidneys

Bile

Bowel   Urine
actions

Toxin List
Metabolic end products, micro-organisms,
contaminants / pollutants, insecticides,
pesticides, food additives, drugs, alcohol

Shoot for Healthy's Pro-Inflammatory Statement
SpectraCell Laboratories Micronutrient Functions, Deficiency and Symptoms

Shoot for Healthy omits grains and dairy from ingredients because of the pro-inflammatory influence of these foods. Gluten and Casein are two of the most common food sensitivities in America. You can develop food sensitivities to just about any food, but foods containing these proteins tend to be a staple in the American diet. Gluten containing foods include wheat, barley, rye, bulgur, couscous, graham flour and many more. It's found in beverages, dressings, sauces, and many processed food products. Casein is found in mainly cow milk products. This includes cheeses, yogurt, milk, cream, butter, margarine spreads, beverages, and processed foods with milk type flavors. Food sensitivities can not only disrupt gut health and immune function, but lead to a cascade of other inflammatory symptoms such as skin rashes, headaches, joint pain, fatigue, hormonal and behavioral imbalances, etc. Cow milk and grains are also high in omega 6 fatty acids. Excessive amounts of omega 6 fats create a pro-inflammatory state in the body. A balance of omega 6 and omega 3 fatty acids is essential for optimal function and health. It's estimated that Americans have a ratio of 23:1 instead of 2:1 omega 6 to 3 fatty acids. We don't necessarily have an omega 3 problem. We have an excessive omega* 6 problem. Shoot for Healthy helps to provide guidance toward a more balanced way of eating to restore optimal health and healing.

Nutrient Functions | Deficiency Symptoms

Micronutrient Testing ✚

NUTRIENT	POTENTIAL	WHAT IT DOES	WHERE IT'S FOUND	SYMPTOMS AND PROBLEMS
VITAMIN E	VERY COMMON	Antioxidant, regulates oxidation reactions, stabilizes cell membrane, immune function, protects against cardiovascular disease, cataracts, macular degeneration	Wheat germ, liver, eggs, nuts, seeds, cold - pressed vegetable oils, dark leafy greens, sweet potatoes, avocados, asparagus	Skin, hair, rupturing of red blood cells, anemia, bruising, PMS, hot flashes, eczema, psoriasis, cataracts, wound healing, muscle weakness, sterility
CALCIUM	VERY COMMON	Bones, teeth, helps heart, nerves, muscles, body systems work properly, needs other nutrients to function	Dairy, wheat/soy flour, molasses, Brewer's yeast, Brazil nuts, broccoli, cabbage, dark leafy greens, hazelnuts, oysters, sardines, canned salmon	Osteoporosis, osteomalacia, osteoarthritis, muscle cramps, irritability, acute anxiety, colon cancer risk
CHROMIUM	COMMON	Assists insulin function, increases fertility, carbohydrate/fat metabolism, essential for fetal growth/development	Supplementation, Brewer's yeast, whole grains, seafood, green beans, broccoli, prunes, nuts, potatoes, meat	Metabolic syndrome, insulin resistance, decreased fertility
MAGNESIUM	VERY COMMON	300 biochemical reactions, muscle/nerve function, heart rhythm, immune system, strong bones, regulates calcium, copper, zinc, potassium, vitamin D	Green vegetables, beans, peas, nuts, seeds, whole unprocessed grains	Appetite, nausea, vomiting, fatigue cramps, numbness, tingling, seizures, heart spasms, personality changes, heart rhythm
SELENIUM	COMMON	Antioxidant, works with vitamin E, immune function, prostaglandin production	Brewer's yeast, wheat germ, liver, butter, cold water fish, shellfish, garlic, whole grains, sunflower seeds, Brazil nuts	Destruction to heart/pancreas, sore muscles, fragility of red blood cells, immune system
ZINC	MOST COMMON	Supports enzymes, immune system, wound healing, taste/smell, DNA synthesis, normal growth & development during pregnancy, childhood and adolescence	Oysters, red meat, poultry, beans, nuts, seafood, whole grains, fortified breakfast cereals, dairy	Growth retardation, hair loss, diarrhea, impotence, eye & skin lesions, loss of appetite, taste, weight loss, wound healing, mental lethargy
CO Q10	COMMON	Powerful antioxidant, stops oxidation of LDL cholesterol, energy production, important to heart, liver and kidneys	Oily fish, organ meats, whole grains	Congestive heart failure, high blood pressure, angina, mitral valve prolapse, fatigue, gingivitis, immune system stroke, cardiac arrhythmias
CARNITINE	LESS COMMON	Energy, heart function, oxidize amino acids for energy, metabolize ketones	Red meat, dairy, fish, poultry, tempeh (fermented soybeans), wheat, asparagus, avocados, peanut butter	Elevated cholesterol, liver function, muscle weakness, reduced energy, impaired glucose control
N - ACETYL CYSTEINE (NAC) & GLUTATHIONE	MOST COMMON	Glutathione production, lowers homocysteine, lipoprotein (a), heal lungs, inflammation, decrease muscle fatigue, liver detoxification, immune function	Meats, ricotta, cottage cheese, yogurt, wheat germ, granola, oat flakes	Free radical overload, elevated homocysteine, cancer risk, cataracts, macular degeneration, immune function, toxin elimination
ALPHA LIPOIC ACID	COMMON	Energy, blood flow to nerves, glutathione levels in brain, insulin sensitivity, effectiveness of vitamins C, E, antioxidants	Supplementation, spinach, broccoli, beef, Brewer's yeast, some organ meats	Diabetic neuropathy, reduced muscle mass, atherosclerosis, Alzheimer's, failure to thrive, brain atrophy, high lactic acid
COPPER	LESS COMMON	Bone formation, involved in healing process, energy production, hair and skin coloring, taste sensitivity, stimulates iron absorption, helps metabolize several fatty acids	Oysters, seeds, dark leafy vegetables, organ meats, dried legumes, whole grain breads, nuts, shellfish, chocolate, soybeans, oats, blackstrap molasses	Osteoporosis, anemia, baldness, diarrhea, general weakness, impaired respiratory function, myelopathy, decreased skin pigment, reduced resistance to infection

© 2011 SpectraCell Laboratories DOC 60 Micronutrient

SpectraCell Laboratories
Science + Health + Solutions

www.SpectraCell.com

Nutrient Deficiency Symptoms
Functions

Micronutrient Testing +

NUTRIENT	POTENTIAL	WHAT IT DOES	WHERE IT'S FOUND	SYMPTOMS AND PROBLEMS
VITAMIN B1	VERY COMMON	Carb. conversion, breaks down fats & protein, digestion, nervous system, skin, hair, eyes, mouth, liver, immune system	Pork, organ meats, whole grain and enriched cereals, brown rice, wheat germ, bran, Brewer's yeast, blackstrap molasses	Heart, age-related cognitive decline, Alzheimer's, fatigue
VITAMIN B2	VERY COMMON	Metabolism, carb. conversion, breaks down fats & protein, digestion, nervous system, skin, hair, eyes, mouth, liver	Brewer's yeast, almonds, organ meats, whole grains, wheat germ, mushrooms, soy, dairy, eggs, green vegetables	Anemia, decreased free radical protection, cataracts, poor thyroid function, B6 deficiency, fatigue, elevated homocysteine
VITAMIN B3	LESS COMMON	Energy, digestion, nervous system, skin, hair, eyes, liver, eliminates toxins, sex/stress hormones, improves circulation	Beets, Brewer's yeast, meat, poultry, organ meats, fish, seeds, nuts	Cracking, scaling skin, digestive problems, confusion, anxiety, fatigue
VITAMIN B6	COMMON	Enzyme, protein metabolism, RBC production, reduces homocysteine, nerve & muscle cells, DNA/RNA, B12 absorption, immune function	Poultry, tuna, salmon, shrimp, beef liver, lentils, soybeans, seeds, nuts, avocados, bananas, carrots, brown rice, bran, wheat germ, whole grain flour	Depression, sleep and skin problems, confusion, anxiety, fatigue
VITAMIN B12	VERY COMMON	Healthy nerve cells, DNA/RNA, red blood cell production, iron function	Fish, meat, poultry, eggs, milk, milk products	Anemia, fatigue, constipation, loss of appetite/weight, numbness and tingling in the hands and feet, depression, dementia, poor memory, oral soreness
BIOTIN	LESS COMMON	Carbs, fat, amino acid metabolism (the building blocks of protein)	Salmon, meats, vegetables, grains, legumes, lentils, egg yolks, milk, sweet potatoes, seeds, nuts, wheat germ	Depression, nervous system, premature graying, hair, skin
FOLATE	VERY COMMON	Mental health, infant DNA/RNA, adolescence & pregnancy, with B12 to regulate RBC production, iron function, reduce homocysteine	Supplementation, fortified grains, tomato juice, green vegetables, black-eyed peas, lentils, beans	Anemia, immune fuction, fatigue, insomnia, hair, high homocysteine, cardiovascular disease
PANTOTHENATE	LESS COMMON	RBC production, sex and stress-related hormones, immune function, healthy digestion, helps use other vitamins	Meat, vegetables, whole grains, legumes, lentils, egg yolks, milk, sweet potatoes, seeds, nuts, wheat germ, salmon	Stress tolerance, wound healing, skin problems, fatigue
VITAMIN A	LESS COMMON	Eyes, immune function, skin, essential cell growth and development	Milk, eggs, liver, fortified cereals, orange or green vegetables, fruits	Night blindness, immune function, zinc deficiency, fat malabsorption
VITAMIN C	COMMON	Enzyme activation, second messenger roles (transmitting hormonal information), blood clotting, cell and cell organelle membrane function, nerve impulse transmission and muscular contraction, tone and irritability	Supplemention, broccoli, brussel sprouts, cantaloupe, cauliflower, citrus, guava, kiwi, papaya, parsley, peas, potatoes, peppers, parsley, rose hips, strawberries and tomatoes	Muscular and nervous irritability, muscle spasms, muscle cramps and tetany, tooth decay, periodontal disease, depression, possibly hypertension
VITAMIN D	VERY COMMON	Calcium and phosphorus levels, calcium absorption, bone mineralization	Sunlight, milk, egg yolks, liver, fish	Osteoporosis, calcium absorption, thyroid
VITAMIN K	LESS COMMON	Aids in the formation of clotting factors and bone proteins and the formation of glucose into glycogen for storage in the liver	Kale, green tea, turnip greens, spinach, broccoli, lettuce, cabbage, beef liver, asparagus, watercress, cheese, oats, peas, whole wheat	Excessive bleeding, a history of bruising, appearance of ruptured capillaries or menorrhagia (heavy periods)

© 2013 SpectraCell Laboratories DOC 501 Micronutrient

SpectraCell Laboratories
Science + Health + Solutions

www.SpectraCell.com

353.

FOODS THAT FIGHT INFLAMMATION

Acai
Almond Butter
Almond
Anchovy
Apples
Asparagus
Avocado Oil
Avocado
Basil
Bee Pollen
Bell Pepper
Black Currant
Blueberry
Bok Choy
Broccoli
Brussels Sprout
Cabbage
Cantaloupe
Cauliflower
Cayenne Pepper
Chard
Cherry
Chicken
Chive
Cilantro
Cinnamon
Cloves
Cocoa
Coconut Oil
Cod
Collard
Cranberry
Cucumber

Cumin Seed
Egg
Extra Virgin Olive Oil
Fennel Bulb
Fig
Flaxseed Oil
Garlic
Ginger
Grape
Green Turnip
Ground Flaxseed
Guava
Hazelnuts
Hemp Seed
Herring
Horseradish
Jicama
Kale
Kelp
Kiwi
Kumquat
Leek
Lemon
Lime
Macadamia
Mint
Mulberry
Mushroom
Olives
Onion
Oregano
Oysters
Papaya

Parsley
Peach
Pea
Pineapple
Plums
Pumpkin
Quail
Radish
Rainbow Trout
Raspberry
Red Beet
Rhubarb
Rosemary
Rutabaga
Salmon (wild)
Sardine
Seaweed
Sesame seed
Spinach
Sprouted Seed
Squash
Strawberry
Tea (white, green, oolong)
Thyme
Tomato
Tuna
Turmeric
Walnut
Watermelon
Wild Game
Yam
Zucchini

NIGHTSHADES

Good: Colorful nightshade vegetables contain Vitamin C and important antioxidants such as lycopene and lutein.

Bad: Nightshade vegetables also contain drug-like chemicals called glycoalkaloids.

Fruits
Goji Berry
Gooseberry (Goldenberry)
Ground Cherry

Naranjillo
Pepino
Tamarillo

Sauces
Ketchup

Tabasco

Spices
Cayenne Pepper
Chili Powder
Chipotle Powder
Curry

Hot Sauce (gluten-free)
Paprika
Red Pepper

Vegetables
Anaheim
Ancho
Bell Peppers
Cascabel
Chile Peppers
Chipotle
Eggplant
Fresno
Garden Huckleberry
Guajillo
Habañero
Italian Peppers
Pasada

Pasilla
Peppers
Pimentos
Poblano
Potatoes
Serrano
Sun-dried Tomatoes
Tamarillos
Tomatillos
Tomatoes
Tomato Paste
Tomato Sauce

*Black Pepper is not considered a nightshade.
*Other: Tobacco

MEASUREMENT CONVERSIONS, U.S. and Metric

U.S.				METRIC
3 teaspoons	1 tablespoon	½ ounce		14.3 grams
2 tablespoons	1/8 cup	1 ounce		28.3 grams
4 tablespoons	1/4 cup	2 ounces		56.7 grams
5 1/3 tablespoons	1/3 cup	2.6 ounces		75.6 grams
8 tablespoons	1/2 cup	4 ounces		113.4 grams
12 tablespoons	3/4 cup	6 ounces		170 grams
16 tablespoons	1 cup	8 ounces	1/2 pound	226.8 grams
32 tablespoons	2 cups	16 ounces	1 pound	453.6 grams
64 tablespoons	4 cups	32 ounces	2 pounds	907.2 grams
1 oz.	2 tablespoons	1/8 cup		30 milliliters
16 oz.	1 pint	2 cups		475 milliliters
32 oz.	1 quart	4 cups		950 milliliters
128 oz	1 gallon	3.75 liters		3750 milliliters
1/2 pound	8 ounces	1 cup		252 grams
1.1 pounds				500 grams
2.2 pounds				1000 grams
[1 kilo]				
8 quarts	1 peck			8.81 liters
4 pecks	1 bushel			35.24 liters
1/4 lb clarified butter/ ghee	1/2 cup	1 stick, unsalted		113.4 grams
1 lb clarified butter/ ghee	2 cups	4 sticks, unsalted		453.6 grams
1 cup	1/2 pint	8 fluid ounces		237 ml
2 cups	1 pint	16 fluid ounces		474 ml
4 cups	1 quart	32 fluid ounces		948 ml
2 pints	1 quart	32 fluid ounces		948 ml
2 quarts	1/2 gallon	64 fluid ounces		1.896 liters
4 quarts	1 gallon	128 fluid ounces		3.792 liters

INTERNAL COOKING TEMPERATURE

GROUND MEAT & MEAT MIXTURES

Beef, Pork, Veal, Lamb (*individually*) - 160°F/ 70°C
Chicken, Turkey (*individually & mixed*) - 165°F/ 75°C
Fresh Beef, Pork, Veal & Lamb (*mixed*) - 165°F/ 75°C

SEAFOOD

Fin Fish - Flesh needs to be opaque and separate easily with a fork
Shrimp, Lobster & Crabs - Flesh pearly & opaque
Clams, Oysters & Mussels - Shells open during cooking
Scallops - Milky White or opaque & firm

EGG AND EGG DISHES

Eggs - Cook until yolk and white are firm
Egg Dishes - 160°F/ 70°C

PORK

Fresh, raw - 160°F/ 70°C
Ham (uncooked) - 145°F/ 63°C
Fully-cooked, reheating - 140°F/ 60°C

POULTRY

Chicken & Turkey, Whole - 165°/ 75°C
Poultry Parts - 165°F/ 75°C
Duck & Goose - 165°F/ 75°C
Stuffing (*in or out of bird*) - 165°F/ 75°C

REHEAT LEFTOVERS - 165°F/ 75°C

BEEF

Rare (120°F to 125°F/ 45°C to 50°C)
Medium-Rare (130°F to 135°F/ 55°C to 60°C)
Medium (140°F to 145°F/ 60°C to 65°C)
Medium-Well (150°F to 155°F/ 65°C to 69°C)
Well-Done (160°F and up/ 70°C and up)

LAMB

Rare (135°F/ 57°C)
Medium-Rare (140°F to 150°F/ 60°C to 65°C)
Medium (150°F to 160°F/ 65°C to 70°C)
Medium-Well (160°F/ 70°C)

LIQUID COOKING TEMPERATURES

LIQUID	F/C	NOTES
Warm Water	115-120°F/46-48°C	Touchable, not hot
Hot Water	130-135°F/54-57°C	Sensitive to touch
Poach	160-180°F/71-82°C	Submerging an item in liquid that is barely simmering
Simmer	185-200°F/85-93°C	Small bubbles begin to rise to the surface
Slow boil	205°F/96°C	Bubbles become larger and movement becomes more rapid

OIL SMOKE POINTS

Smoke points tell us how high specific oils can be heated before they break down, actually smoking.

When oil is heated past its smoke point, the fat will break down and releases free radical and acrolein. Acrolein is a chemical giving burnt foods their bitter flavor and aroma.

TYPE OF FAT	SMOKE POINT	REFINED
Avocado Oil (Virgin)	375-400°F/190-205°C	No
Beef Tallow	400°F/250°C	No
Butter	350°F/175°C	No; grain-fed dairy
Canola Oil	400°F/205°C	Yes
Chicken Fat (Schmaltz)	375°F/190°C	No
Clarified Butter	450°F/230°C	No
Coconut Oil	350°F/175°C	No
Duck Fat	375°F/190°C	No
Extra-Virgin Olive Oil	325°F-375°F/165-190°C	No
Grapeseed Oil	390°F/195°C	Yes
Lard	370°F/185°C	Yes
Light/Refined Olive Oil	465°F/240°C	Yes
Rice Bran Oil	490°F/260°C	Yes
Safflower Oil, High Oleic	510° F/265°C	Yes
Sesame Oil	350-410°F/175-210°C	No
Sunflower Oil	440°F/225°C	Yes
Vegetable Oil	400-450°F/205-230°C	Yes
Vegetable Shortening	360°F/180°C	Yes

OIL SMOKE POINT TIPS

Clarified butter, or ghee, have higher smoke points due to the exclusion of heat-sensitive components from the fat; in this case, milk solids.

The following flavor oils should be refrigerated: avocado, hazelnut, sesame, and walnut oils.

Do NOT store oils over the stove. Heat can lead to an oils rancidity/spoilage.

Always keep your oils tightly sealed and in a cool, dark place. It's best to buy in darker bottles protected from sunlight. If you purchase a translucent bottle, Wrap it in tin foil to extend shelf life. Purchasing pure oils in dark bottles is best.

PRODUCT RECOMMENDATIONS

1. <u>Creamy Almond Butter</u>, Barney's or Maranatha brand; available at grocery stores nationwide.
2. <u>Mother's Apple Cider Vinegar</u>, Unpasteurized, Braggs Mother's Apple Cider Vinegar (yellow label), available at grocery stores nationwide.
3. <u>Coconut Aminos</u>, available at health food grocery stores nationwide.
4. <u>Coconut Sugar</u>, available at grocery stores nationwide.
5. <u>Organic Ginger Spread</u>, The Ginger People
6. <u>Extra Virgin Olive Oil, Kasandrinos</u> - Receive 10% off your total; **Coupon Code: agogefuel, kasandrinos.com,** Origin: Greece, Shipped worldwide from USA Headquarters
7. <u>Paleo Powder</u>, paleopowder.com; Seasoning for everything. great people, great product.
8. <u>Tahini Sauce, Vitacost Certified Organic Unsalted Sesame Tahini</u>; available at grocery stores nationwide, on the condiment, sauce aisle. Or you can Google and find it online.

Anytime you buy products, you should look at the ingredients list. If it has more "stuff" than it says on the label, it's more than likely no good, and will have an abundance of inflammatory ingredients, mostly in the ones you cannot pronounce.

Watch out for "gluten-free" products. Gluten-free products may have minimal gluten; yet, they are loaded with indigestible carbs and sugars, to make up the difference. The FDA Gluten-free labeling allows manufacturers to claim this label, so long as their product has less than 20 parts per million, ppm. This equates to .002%, which does not take into account any possible gluten contamination; 20 milligrams of gluten per 35.27 ounces of food; this seems rather small, and it is, except when you are gluten intolerant or have celiac disease, this can be devastating for you.

If a product contains even the smallest amount, this could possibly be enough to trigger your body's negative reaction to gluten. Gluten intolerance affects most people since our body's ability to digest is not available. Gluten refers to the protein found in wheat endosperm; applicable in products containing Wheat, Barley, Rye, and Triticale.

Remember, labels do not tell you the full details. Just because something claims to be gluten free, most times that is not the case. The FDA requiring a product to contain 20 ppm or less, meaning that there is a chance of gluten contamination, especially for products made in the same facility that manufactures these products.

BUYING GUIDE, for Healthier hoices

Beef	• **Grass-fed – Best choice**
	• 93/7 or 94/6 – Best of grain fed beef
	• We want LEAN grain-fed meat, the less fat the better. (no more 80/20)
	• Grain-fed cows are fattened up with non-nutrient foods at 90-120 days to harvest. These foods prohibit digestion of nutrients and, like us, store as fat. The process is replicated, as we also store fat from non-nutrient foods.
Chicken	• **Free-range; no grain or casein**
Turkey	• **Free-range; no grain or casein**
Pork	• Uncured, Nitrite and Nitrate free
	• Applegate is a good brand for sliced deli meats and bacon; uncured.
Seafood	• **Wild-Caught**
	• Refer to NOAA.com when for purchasing seafood; looking for any possible oceanic contaminations.
Vegetables & Fruits	• **Refer to The Dirty Dozen and Clean 15, *page 15*.**
	• If you have the ability to grow these at your home, please DO! We promote home grown organic gardening. Homegrown produce ALWAYS tastes better.
	Other locations, in order:
	• *Farmers Markets*
	• *Grocery Store* - choose organic whenever possible, especially The Dirty Dozen.
	• *Frozen*
	• *Organic Cans and Jars* – stay away from cans and jars as much as possible. You can usually find organic products for most products, if can is needed. Be sure to check the label for products containing only real ingredients; natural and artificial flavoring is not real food). Home products like jams, preserves and fermented products sold at Farmers Markets can still be loaded with the wrong sugars; organic or not.
Resource *EatWild.com* for help in finding local farmers markets, fresh eggs, meat, chicken, turkey, pork, lamb, wild game…you name it.	

NOTES

CPSIA information can be obtained at www.ICGtesting.com
Printed in the USA
LVOW05*0044101015

457686LV00003B/3/P